SCOTT FORESMAN

Reading Street

COMMON CORE

Reading Street Common Core
Writing to Sources

Glenview, Illinois

Boston, Massachusetts

Chandler, Arizona

Upper Saddle River, New Jersey

W9-CYG-679

PEARSON

ISBN-13: 978-0-328-76854-7
ISBN-10: 0-328-76854-5
5 6 7 8 9 10 V0N4 16 15 14 13

Reading Street Common Core
Writing to Sources

Reading Street Common Core Writing to Sources makes fact-finding fun! Students substantiate their claims and communicate in writing what they have learned from one text and then from other related texts.

Reading Street Common Core Writing to Sources encourages students to collaborate and share their growing knowledge with peers, adding quality experiences in the art of using text-based evidence.

Reading Street Common Core Writing to Sources provides more practice with all modes of writing—argument, informative/explanatory, and narrative—and connects to the Common Core State Standards.

Reading Street Common Core Writing to Sources gives students opportunities to complete Performance Tasks by writing in response to what they read and collaborating with others.

Reading Street Common Core Writing to Sources offers you an alternative approach to writing tasks on Reading Street!

1 Write Like a Reporter
Write to one source.
Students respond to the main selection by citing evidence from the text.

2 Connect the Texts
Write to two sources.
Students respond to the main and paired selections by citing evidence from the texts.

3 Prove It! Unit Writing Task
Write to multiple sources.
Students analyze multiple sources within a unit and cite evidence from the texts.

4 More Connect the Texts
Additional lessons specific to writing forms within all modes of writing—argument, informative/explanatory, and narrative—are included.

"Write Like a Reporter!"

Table of Contents

Get Ready for Performance Tasks

Table of Contents

More Connect the Texts   221

Writing Forms

Unit 1 All Together Now

Writing Focus: Narrative

Name_____

Write Like a Reporter
Narrative

Student Prompt Look at pages 24–25 of *The Little School Bus*. Tell how the animal characters get to school. Use details from the story and the pictures. Write about it.

_____

- -

_____

- -

_____

- -

_____

- -

_____

- -

_____

- -

_____

Write Like a Reporter
Narrative

> **Student Prompt, p. 6** Look at pages 24–25 of *The Little School Bus*. Tell how the animal characters get to school. Use details from the story and the pictures. Write about it.

Writing to Sources Have children look at the story and write about it. Point out that the characters in the story ride a bus to school. Have children look at the pictures to learn ways some of the other characters get to school. Turn to pp. 24–25. Discuss with children other ways the animals are getting to school and record children's responses on chart paper. (A duck walks to school. Some rabbits bike to school. Some birds drive to school.)

Then ask children to look at the pictures on pp. 24–25 again and add details to the sentences by using words that describe the characters. Point to the sentence about the duck and ask, "What color word can we add to the sentence to describe the duck?" Write the sentence (A yellow duck walks to school.) and read it with children. Continue by having children write or dictate another sentence with details to create a description of an animal and how it gets to school.

Children's sentences should:
- provide a setting and character
- include events that reflect those in the text
- use details to elaborate on the events
- demonstrate strong command of the conventions of standard written English

ⓒ **Common Core State Standards**

Writing 3. Use a combination of drawing, dictating, and writing to narrate a single event or several loosely linked events, tell about the events in the order in which they occurred, and provide a reaction to what happened.

Narrative

The Little School Bus

Name_____

Connect the Texts
Narrative

Student Prompt What happens first, next, and last in these stories:

The Little School Bus
"King Midas and the Golden Touch"

Tell what happens in each story. Write the first event in the story you choose.

_____

_____

_____

_____

_____

_____

_____

_____

_____

_____

8 Unit 1 • Week 1 • *The Little School Bus*

Copyright © Pearson Education, Inc., or its affiliates. All Rights Reserved.

Connect the Texts
Narrative

Student Prompt, p. 8 What happens first, next, and last in these stories:

The Little School Bus

"King Midas and the Golden Touch"

Tell what happens in each story. Write the first event in the story you choose.

Writing to Sources Have children think about the order of events in *The Little School Bus* and in "King Midas and the Golden Touch" on pp. 101 and 108a of the Teacher's Edition. Have children tell the order in which the animals got on the school bus. Display the pictures in *The Little School Bus* and ask, "Who got on the bus first?" Write a sentence to tell about each animal using the following sentence frame: _____ *got on the bus* _____. Then ask children to retell the story of King Midas. Have them look at the pictures on pp. 30–31 in *My Skills Buddy* and have them describe each picture in one or two sentences. Record their responses on chart paper. Then ask children to choose one story and write or dictate a sentence that tells what happens first in that story.

	4-point Narrative Writing Rubric				
Score	**Narrative Focus**	**Organization**	**Development of Narrative**	**Language and Vocabulary**	**Conventions**
4	Narrative is clearly focused and developed throughout.	Narrative has a well-developed, logical, easy-to-follow plot.	Narrative includes thorough and effective use of details, dialogue, and description.	Narrative uses precise, concrete sensory language as well as figurative language and/or domain-specific vocabulary.	Narrative has correct grammar, usage, spelling, capitalization, and punctuation.
3	Narrative is mostly focused and developed throughout.	Narrative has a plot, but there may be some lack of clarity and/or unrelated events.	Narrative includes adequate use of details, dialogue and description.	Narrative uses adequate sensory and figurative language and/or domain-specific vocabulary.	Narrative has a few errors but is completely understandable.
2	Narrative is somewhat developed but may occasionally lose focus.	Narrative's plot is difficult to follow, and ideas are not connected well.	Narrative includes only a few details, dialogues, and description.	Language in narrative is not precise or sensory; lacks domain-specific vocabulary.	Narrative has some errors in usage, grammar, spelling and/or punctuation.
1	Narrative may be confusing, unfocused, or too short.	Narrative has little or no apparent plot.	Narrative includes few or no details, dialogue or description.	Language in narrative is vague, unclear, or confusing.	Narrative is hard to follow because of frequent errors.
0	Narrative gets no credit if it does not demonstrate adequate command of narrative writing traits.				

© Common Core State Standards

Writing 3. Use a combination of drawing, dictating, and writing to narrate a single event or several loosely linked events, tell about the events in the order in which they occurred, and provide a reaction to what happened.

Write Like a Reporter

Narrative

Student Prompt Look at the text and the pictures on pages 8–14 of *We Are So Proud!* Write about the children making a flag.

_____

_____

_____

_____

_____

_____

_____

_____

Write Like a Reporter
Narrative

> **Student Prompt, p. 10** Look at the text and the pictures on pages 8–14 of *We Are So Proud!* Write about the children making a flag.

Writing to Sources Have children look at the characters in the story. Remind them that the children in Ms. Vogel's class work together on a special project. As you read, have them listen for ways the characters work on the float and look at the illustrations to see what the class does. Guide children to notice the expressions on the children's faces on pp. 8–14. Ask: "What can you tell about the children as they are working on the float?" Record their responses on chart paper (having fun; happy; working together; smiling). Work with children to complete the following sentence frame with ideas from the list: *The children are _____.* Have children illustrate their sentence.

Children's sentences should:
- provide details about characters
- include a logical sequence of events that reflects those in the text
- use details to elaborate on the events
- demonstrate strong command of the conventions of standard written English

Ⓒ **Common Core State Standards**

Writing 3. Use a combination of drawing, dictating, and writing to narrate a single event or several loosely linked events, tell about the events in the order in which they occurred, and provide a reaction to what happened.

Name_____

Connect the Texts
Narrative

> **Student Prompt** Read about flags in these selections:
>
> *We Are So Proud!*
>
> "The United States Flag"
>
> Write about the flags.

_____

- - - - - - - - - - - - - - - - - - - -

_____

- - - - - - - - - - - - - - - - - - - -

_____

- - - - - - - - - - - - - - - - - - - -

_____

- - - - - - - - - - - - - - - - - - - -

_____

- - - - - - - - - - - - - - - - - - - -

_____

- - - - - - - - - - - - - - - - - - - -

_____

- - - - - - - - - - - - - - - - - - - -

_____

- - - - - - - - - - - - - - - - - - - -

_____

- - - - - - - - - - - - - - - - - - - -

_____

Connect the Texts
Narrative

> **Student Prompt, p. 12** Read about flags in these selections:
>
> *We Are So Proud!*
>
> "The United States Flag"
>
> Write about the flags.

Writing to Sources The story *We Are So Proud!* tells about a time when the children in Ms. Vogel's class make a flag for a parade. "The United States Flag" (on page 197 of the Teacher's Edition) describes how the U.S. flag looked when it was first made and how it looks today. Ask children to describe the flag (using color and shape words). Make a list of their describing words. Then have them use this sentence frame to write or dictate a sentence about the flag: *The flag _____*.

4-point Narrative Writing Rubric					
Score	**Narrative Focus**	**Organization**	**Development of Narrative**	**Language and Vocabulary**	**Conventions**
4	Narrative is clearly focused and developed throughout.	Narrative has a well-developed, logical, easy-to-follow plot.	Narrative includes thorough and effective use of details, dialogue, and description.	Narrative uses precise, concrete sensory language as well as figurative language and/or domain-specific vocabulary.	Narrative has correct grammar, usage, spelling, capitalization, and punctuation.
3	Narrative is mostly focused and developed throughout.	Narrative has a plot, but there may be some lack of clarity and/or unrelated events.	Narrative includes adequate use of details, dialogue and description.	Narrative uses adequate sensory and figurative language and/or domain-specific vocabulary.	Narrative has a few errors but is completely understandable.
2	Narrative is somewhat developed but may occasionally lose focus.	Narrative's plot is difficult to follow, and ideas are not connected well.	Narrative includes only a few details, dialogues, and description.	Language in narrative is not precise or sensory; lacks domain-specific vocabulary.	Narrative has some errors in usage, grammar, spelling and/or punctuation.
1	Narrative may be confusing, unfocused, or too short.	Narrative has little or no apparent plot.	Narrative includes few or no details, dialogue or description.	Language in narrative is vague, unclear, or confusing.	Narrative is hard to follow because of frequent errors.
0	Narrative gets no credit if it does not demonstrate adequate command of narrative writing traits.				

© Common Core State Standards

Writing 3. Use a combination of drawing, dictating, and writing to narrate a single event or several loosely linked events, tell about the events in the order in which they occurred, and provide a reaction to what happened.

Name_____

Write Like a Reporter
Narrative

Student Prompt Look at pages 20–21 in *Plaidypus Lost*. What words tell where the girl looks? Write about where she looks.

_____

- -

_____

- -

_____

- -

_____

- -

_____

- -

_____

- -

_____

- -

_____

Write Like a Reporter
Narrative

> **Student Prompt, p. 14** Look at pages 20–21 in *Plaidypus Lost*. What words tell where the girl looks? Write about where she looks.

Writing to Sources Have children look back at *Plaidypus Lost* and write about it. Remind them that the girl loses Plaidypus in the grocery store. Ask them to listen for where she looks for Plaidypus and to remember the words that give details to tell where she looks. Reread pp. 20–21 of *Plaidypus Lost*. Discuss with children the directions the girl looks in when she realizes Plaidypus is missing. Record their responses on chart paper. (She looks left and right. She looks high and low. She looks over and under.) Reread the sentences together and have children act out what the girl does. Have children choose one sentence to write and illustrate.

Children's sentences should:

- provide a setting and character
- include a logical sequence of events that reflect those in the text
- use detail words to identify the order of events
- demonstrate strong command of the conventions of standard written English

Ⓒ **Common Core State Standards**

Writing 3. Use a combination of drawing, dictating, and writing to narrate a single event or several loosely linked events, tell about the events in the order in which they occurred, and provide a reaction to what happened.

Name_____

Connect the Texts

Narrative

> **Student Prompt** Read about a girl and a boy in these selections:
>
> *Plaidypus Lost*
> "The Boy Who Cried 'Wolf'"
>
> What does each child do again and again? Write about what they do.

_____

- -

_____

- -

_____

- -

_____

- -

_____

- -

_____

Connect the Texts
Narrative

Student Prompt, p. 16 Read about a girl and a boy in these selections:

Plaidypus Lost

"The Boy Who Cried 'Wolf'"

What does each child do again and again? Write about what they do.

Writing to Sources Ask: "What does the girl do again and again in *Plaidypus Lost?* What does the boy do again and again in "The Boy Who Cried Wolf?" Write the following sentence frames: *The girl _____ again and again. The boy _____ again and again*. Ask children to tell ways to complete the sentences. Record their responses on chart paper. Then have them use the sentences on the chart for ideas to write or dictate their own sentences about the girl and the boy.

4-point Narrative Writing Rubric					
Score	**Narrative Focus**	**Organization**	**Development of Narrative**	**Language and Vocabulary**	**Conventions**
4	Narrative is clearly focused and developed throughout.	Narrative has a well-developed, logical, easy-to-follow plot.	Narrative includes thorough and effective use of details, dialogue, and description.	Narrative uses precise, concrete sensory language as well as figurative language and/or domain-specific vocabulary.	Narrative has correct grammar, usage, spelling, capitalization, and punctuation.
3	Narrative is mostly focused and developed throughout.	Narrative has a plot, but there may be some lack of clarity and/or unrelated events.	Narrative includes adequate use of details, dialogue and description.	Narrative uses adequate sensory and figurative language and/or domain-specific vocabulary.	Narrative has a few errors but is completely understandable.
2	Narrative is somewhat developed but may occasionally lose focus.	Narrative's plot is difficult to follow, and ideas are not connected well.	Narrative includes only a few details, dialogues, and description.	Language in narrative is not precise or sensory; lacks domain-specific vocabulary.	Narrative has some errors in usage, grammar, spelling and/or punctuation.
1	Narrative may be confusing, unfocused, or too short.	Narrative has little or no apparent plot.	Narrative includes few or no details, dialogue or description.	Language in narrative is vague, unclear, or confusing.	Narrative is hard to follow because of frequent errors.
0	Narrative gets no credit if it does not demonstrate adequate command of narrative writing traits.				

ⓒ Common Core State Standards

Writing 3. Use a combination of drawing, dictating, and writing to narrate a single event or several loosely linked events, tell about the events in the order in which they occurred, and provide a reaction to what happened.

Write Like a Reporter
Narrative

Student Prompt Look at the text and the pictures on pages 24–25 in *Miss Bindergarten Takes a Field Trip*. Write about the things the children can do at the library.

_____

- -

_____

- -

_____

- -

_____

- -

_____

- -

_____

- -

_____

- -

_____

- -

_____

Write Like a Reporter
Narrative

> **Student Prompt, p. 18** Look at the text and the pictures on pages 24–25 in *Miss Bindergarten Takes a Field Trip*. Write about the things the children can do at the library.

Writing to Sources Reread pp. 24–25 of *Miss Bindergarten Takes a Field Trip*. Tell children to listen to the story and look at the pictures. Explain that the library is one place Miss Bindergarten's class visits. Have children look at the pictures to see what things Miss Bindergarten's class does at a library. Then ask children to share their ideas. If needed, record children's responses on chart paper. (The children can sit. The children can read. The children can choose books. The children can use computers.) Have children write or dictate a sentence that tells what the class does at the library. Ask volunteers to share their sentences.

Children's sentences should:

- provide a setting
- include a logical sequence of events that reflects those in the text
- use detail and descriptive words to tell about the events
- demonstrate strong command of the conventions of standard written English

Ⓒ Common Core State Standards

Writing 3. Use a combination of drawing, dictating, and writing to narrate a single event or several loosely linked events, tell about the events in the order in which they occurred, and provide a reaction to what happened.

Connect the Texts
Narrative

Student Prompt Tell about the events in these selections:

Miss Bindergarten Takes a Field Trip
"Curry Veggie Dip"

Write a make-believe story about Miss Bindergarten's class making curry veggie dip.

_____
- -
_____
- -
_____
- -
_____
- -
_____
- -
_____
- -
_____

Connect the Texts
Narrative

Student Prompt, p. 20 Tell about the events in these selections:

Miss Bindergarten Takes a Field Trip

"Curry Veggie Dip"

Write a make-believe story about Miss Bindergarten's class making curry veggie dip.

Writing to Sources Have children review the places Miss Bindergarten's class goes on their field trip. Then have them look at the pictures on pp. 90–91 in *My Skills Buddy* and tell about making curry veggie dip. Have children write a make-believe story about Miss Bindergarten's class making a curry veggie dip. Record the story on chart paper for children to copy. Suggest children use words and pictures from the selections to help them write the story. Have children draw a picture to illustrate their story.

Score	\multicolumn{5}{c}{4-point Narrative Writing Rubric}
	Narrative Focus	**Organization**	**Development of Narrative**	**Language and Vocabulary**	**Conventions**
4	Narrative is clearly focused and developed throughout.	Narrative has a well-developed, logical, easy-to-follow plot.	Narrative includes thorough and effective use of details, dialogue, and description.	Narrative uses precise, concrete sensory language as well as figurative language and/or domain-specific vocabulary.	Narrative has correct grammar, usage, spelling, capitalization, and punctuation.
3	Narrative is mostly focused and developed throughout.	Narrative has a plot, but there may be some lack of clarity and/or unrelated events.	Narrative includes adequate use of details, dialogue and description.	Narrative uses adequate sensory and figurative language and/or domain-specific vocabulary.	Narrative has a few errors but is completely understandable.
2	Narrative is somewhat developed but may occasionally lose focus.	Narrative's plot is difficult to follow, and ideas are not connected well.	Narrative includes only a few details, dialogues, and description.	Language in narrative is not precise or sensory; lacks domain-specific vocabulary.	Narrative has some errors in usage, grammar, spelling and/or punctuation.
1	Narrative may be confusing, unfocused, or too short.	Narrative has little or no apparent plot.	Narrative includes few or no details, dialogue or description.	Language in narrative is vague, unclear, or confusing.	Narrative is hard to follow because of frequent errors.
0	\multicolumn{5}{l}{Narrative gets no credit if it does not demonstrate adequate command of narrative writing traits.}

© Common Core State Standards

Writing 3. Use a combination of drawing, dictating, and writing to narrate a single event or several loosely linked events, tell about the events in the order in which they occurred, and provide a reaction to what happened.

Name_____

Write Like a Reporter
Narrative

Student Prompt Look at the text and pictures on pp. 16–20 in *Smash! Crash!* Name the reasons why Max can't play. Write about how Jack and Dan help.

_____

- -

_____

- -

_____

- -

_____

- -

_____

- -

_____

- -

_____

- -

_____

- -

_____

Write Like a Reporter
Narrative

Student Prompt, p. 22 Look at the text and pictures on pp. 16–20 in *Smash! Crash!* Name the reasons why Max can't play. Write about how Jack and Dan help.

Writing to Sources Reread pp. 16–20 of *Smash! Crash!* Remind children that Jack and Dan want Monster Truck Max to help them smash and crash, but he is busy. Ask children to listen for what Max has to do. Discuss with children why Max can't play. Then have them tell how Jack and Dan help him. Record children's responses on chart paper. (Max must stack barrels by two. Jack and Dan smash and crash. The barrels are smacked, whacked, and stacked.) Have children write or dictate sentences about how Jack and Dan help.

Children's sentences should:

- provide a setting, the characters, and the events
- include a logical sequence of events that reflects those in the text
- use time-order words that signify the order of events
- demonstrate strong command of the conventions of standard written English

Ⓒ **Common Core State Standards**

Writing 3. Use a combination of drawing, dictating, and writing to narrate a single event or several loosely linked events, tell about the events in the order in which they occurred, and provide a reaction to what happened.

Connect the Texts

Narrative

> **Student Prompt** Look at the pictures and read the text in each of these stories:
>
> _Smash! Crash!_
> "At a Farmer's Market"
>
> Write a story about Dan and Jack going to the farmer's market. What do you think might happen?

_____

_____

_____

_____

_____

_____

_____

_____

_____

_____

_____

_____

Connect the Texts
Narrative

> **Student Prompt, p. 24** Look at the pictures and read the text in each of these stories:
>
> *Smash! Crash!*
>
> "At a Farmer's Market"
>
> Write a story about Dan and Jack going to the farmer's market. What do you think might happen?

Writing to Sources Reread *Smash! Crash!* and "At a Farmer's Market" with children. Discuss what Jack and Dan do in *Smash! Crash!* Then direct them to look at the pictures in "At a Farmer's Market" in *My Skills Buddy,* pp. 110–111. Ask children what might have to change in the pictures if Jack and Dan visited the farmer's market. Have children work together to write a story about what Jack and Dan might do at the farmer's market. Remind children to use the selections to help them with their ideas. Write their story on chart paper for them to copy. Have them draw a picture to illustrate the story.

4-point Narrative Writing Rubric					
Score	Narrative Focus	Organization	Development of Narrative	Language and Vocabulary	Conventions
4	Narrative is clearly focused and developed throughout.	Narrative has a well-developed, logical, easy-to-follow plot.	Narrative includes thorough and effective use of details, dialogue, and description.	Narrative uses precise, concrete sensory language as well as figurative language and/or domain-specific vocabulary.	Narrative has correct grammar, usage, spelling, capitalization, and punctuation.
3	Narrative is mostly focused and developed throughout.	Narrative has a plot, but there may be some lack of clarity and/or unrelated events.	Narrative includes adequate use of details, dialogue and description.	Narrative uses adequate sensory and figurative language and/or domain-specific vocabulary.	Narrative has a few errors but is completely understandable.
2	Narrative is somewhat developed but may occasionally lose focus.	Narrative's plot is difficult to follow, and ideas are not connected well.	Narrative includes only a few details, dialogues, and description.	Language in narrative is not precise or sensory; lacks domain-specific vocabulary.	Narrative has some errors in usage, grammar, spelling and/or punctuation.
1	Narrative may be confusing, unfocused, or too short.	Narrative has little or no apparent plot.	Narrative includes few or no details, dialogue or description.	Language in narrative is vague, unclear, or confusing.	Narrative is hard to follow because of frequent errors.
0	Narrative gets no credit if it does not demonstrate adequate command of narrative writing traits.				

© Common Core State Standards

Writing 3. Use a combination of drawing, dictating, and writing to narrate a single event or several loosely linked events, tell about the events in the order in which they occurred, and provide a reaction to what happened.

Write Like a Reporter
Narrative

Student Prompt Look at the machines in *Dig Dig Digging*. Choose a machine from the story. Who is using that machine? Write about what that person is doing.

_____

- -

_____

- -

_____

- -

_____

- -

_____

- -

_____

- -

_____

- -

_____

- -

_____

Write Like a Reporter
Narrative

> **Student Prompt, p. 26** Look at the machines in *Dig Dig Digging*. Choose a machine from the story. Who is using that machine? Write about what that person is doing.

Writing to Sources Display the book *Dig Dig Digging*. Have children review the selection, name the machines, and tell what each one does. Then ask children to choose a page from the selection and write or dictate sentences telling what is happening on the page. Have children tell who is using the machine and what that person is doing. Suggest that they include words to tell about the machine's size and shape.

Children's sentences should:

- provide a setting and purpose
- include events that reflect those in the text
- use details and time-order words that elaborate the sequence of events
- demonstrate strong command of the conventions of standard written English

Ⓒ **Common Core State Standards**

Writing 3. Use a combination of drawing, dictating, and writing to narrate a single event or several loosely linked events, tell about the events in the order in which they occurred, and provide a reaction to what happened.

Name_____

Connect the Texts
Narrative

Student Prompt Read these selections.
Dig Dig Digging
"The Three Little Pigs"
Tell about each selection. Write or dictate what happens last in each selection.

_____

_____

_____

_____

_____

_____

_____

_____

Connect the Texts
Narrative

Student Prompt, p. 28 Read these selections.

Dig Dig Digging

"The Three Little Pigs"

Tell about each selection. Write or dictate what happens last in each selection.

Writing to Sources Have children look at the illustrations on pp. 130–131 in *My Skills Buddy* and retell the events of the "The Three Little Pigs." Write their responses on sentence strips. Be sure to display the sentences in the correct order of events to retell the story. Have children talk about the machines in *Dig Dig Digging*. Then have them look at the picture on pp. 26–27 and tell what is shown in the sky. (stars) Explain that this shows nighttime and is the last event in the selection. Talk about what the trucks are doing. Write children's responses on chart paper. Use this sentence frame: *At night, all the machines* _____. Then have children write or dictate sentences that tell what happens last in each story.

	4-point Narrative Writing Rubric				
Score	**Narrative Focus**	**Organization**	**Development of Narrative**	**Language and Vocabulary**	**Conventions**
4	Narrative is clearly focused and developed throughout.	Narrative has a well-developed, logical, easy-to-follow plot.	Narrative includes thorough and effective use of details, dialogue, and description.	Narrative uses precise, concrete sensory language as well as figurative language and/or domain-specific vocabulary.	Narrative has correct grammar, usage, spelling, capitalization, and punctuation.
3	Narrative is mostly focused and developed throughout.	Narrative has a plot, but there may be some lack of clarity and/or unrelated events.	Narrative includes adequate use of details, dialogue and description.	Narrative uses adequate sensory and figurative language and/or domain-specific vocabulary.	Narrative has a few errors but is completely understandable.
2	Narrative is somewhat developed but may occasionally lose focus.	Narrative's plot is difficult to follow, and ideas are not connected well.	Narrative includes only a few details, dialogues, and description.	Language in narrative is not precise or sensory; lacks domain-specific vocabulary.	Narrative has some errors in usage, grammar, spelling and/or punctuation.
1	Narrative may be confusing, unfocused, or too short.	Narrative has little or no apparent plot.	Narrative includes few or no details, dialogue or description.	Language in narrative is vague, unclear, or confusing.	Narrative is hard to follow because of frequent errors.
0	Narrative gets no credit if it does not demonstrate adequate command of narrative writing traits.				

Ⓒ Common Core State Standards

Writing 3. Use a combination of drawing, dictating, and writing to narrate a single event or several loosely linked events, tell about the events in the order in which they occurred, and provide a reaction to what happened.

Prove It!
Story

Academic Vocabulary

A story tells about characters. It tells what the characters do.

ELL

Introduce Genre Write *story* on the board. Explain that this word is used to identify writing about someone or something. It tells about the people in the story, and it tells what they do. The people or animals are called characters. Discuss with children the key features of a story that appear on this page.

What Characters Do

Story

In this unit, children have read examples of narrative writing and have had the opportunity to write in this mode. Remind children of texts and writing tasks (such as Write Like a Reporter) in which they have encountered and practiced narrative writing.

Key Features of a Story

- has a beginning, middle, and end
- uses characters to tell the story
- tells about an interesting event
- includes detail words to describe characters and events

Writing Task Overview

Each unit writing task provides children with an opportunity to write using information from a selection they are reading. To successfully complete the task, children must understand and interpret the selection and create their own response.

What Characters Do

Part 1: Children will reread a selection identified from this unit. They will then respond to the selection and discuss their written response with partners.

Part 2: Children will work individually to plan, write, and revise their own story.

Scorable Products: evidence-based short response, story

What Characters Do: Writing Task – Short Response

Teacher Directions:

1. Introduce the Source Reread the following Big Book selection:

Smash! Crash!

Explain to children that they will use the words and illustrations in the book to respond. Tell children that they will also write their own stories that use information from the text.

2. Have children draw a picture of one character in *Smash! Crash!*

3. Using evidence from the text, have children write or dictate an event from the story involving the character they have chosen.

© **Common Core State Standards**

Writing 3. Use a combination of drawing, dictating, and writing to narrate a single event or several loosely linked events, tell about the events in the order in which they occurred, and provide a reaction to what happened.

Scoring Information

Use the following 2-point scoring rubric to evaluate children's answers to the evidence-based short response.

Analysis Rubric	
2	The response: • demonstrates the ability to analyze story details in order to describe a character • includes specific details that make reference to the text
1	The response: • demonstrates a limited ability to analyze story details in order to describe a character • includes some details that make reference to the text
0	A response receives no credit if it demonstrates no ability to analyze story details or includes no relevant details from the text.

© **Common Core State Standards**

Writing 3. Use a combination of drawing, dictating, and writing to narrate a single event or several loosely linked events, tell about the events in the order in which they occurred, and provide a reaction to what happened.

Name _____

What Characters Do

Writing Task – Short Response

Draw a picture of a character from
Smash! Crash!

Name _____

Write a sentence about the character.

_____

- -

_____

- -

_____

- -

_____

- -

_____

- -

_____

- -

_____

- -

_____

What Characters Do: Writing Task – Story

Teacher Directions:

1. Have children draw a picture of a character from the story *Smash! Crash!*

2. Have children write or dictate an event from the story involving the character.

3. Scoring Information Use the scoring rubric on the next page to evaluate children's stories.

Ⓒ **Common Core State Standards**

Writing 3. Use a combination of drawing, dictating, and writing to narrate a single event or several loosely linked events, tell about the events in the order in which they occurred, and provide a reaction to what happened.

Score	Narrative Focus	Organization	Development of Narrative	Language and Vocabulary	Conventions
4	Narrative clearly tells what the character does.	Narrative has an easy-to-follow event (plot).	Narrative includes effective use of details.	Narrative uses sensory language.	Narrative has correct use of conventions.
3	Narrative tells what the character does.	Narrative has an event (plot).	Narrative includes adequate use of details.	Narrative uses some sensory language.	Narrative has a few errors but is completely understandable.
2	Narrative may tell a little about what the character does.	Narrative's event is confusing.	Narrative includes only a few details.	Language in narrative is not sensory.	Narrative has some errors in standard conventions.
1	Narrative may be confusing.	Narrative has little or no apparent plot.	Narrative includes few or no details.	Language in narrative is confusing.	Narrative is hard to follow because of frequent errors.
0	Narrative gets no credit if it does not demonstrate adequate command of narrative writing traits.				

Narrative Writing Rubric

Ⓒ Common Core State Standards

Writing 3. Use a combination of drawing, dictating, and writing to narrate a single event or several loosely linked events, tell about the events in the order in which they occurred, and provide a reaction to what happened.

Name _____

What Characters Do
Writing Task – Story

Story Prompt

Draw a picture of a character from *Smash! Crash!*
Write a story about the character. Your story
should tell what the character does.

Name _____

What Characters Do: Writing Task – Story

Teacher Directions:

1. Publish Explain to children that publishing their writing is the last step in the writing process. If time permits, have children review one another's stories and incorporate any comments their classmates have. Discuss different ways technology can be used to publish writing.

2. Present Children will now have the option to present their stories. Have children tell about their stories in front of the class. Use the list below to offer children some tips on listening and speaking.

While Listening to a Classmate...
- Face the speaker to listen attentively.
- Think about what the speaker says.

While Speaking to Classmates...
- Have good posture and eye contact.
- Speak at an appropriate pace.

Things to Do Together...
- Ask and answer questions with detail.
- Build on each other's ideas.

© Common Core State Standards

Writing 3. Use a combination of drawing, dictating, and writing to narrate a single event or several loosely linked events, tell about the events in the order in which they occurred, and provide a reaction to what happened.

Unit 2 Look at Us!

Writing Focus: Informative/Explanatory

Name_____

Write Like a Reporter

Informative/Explanatory

Student Prompt Look at pages 4–5 in *Flowers*. Tell why flowers are important. Write what you learned.

_____

- -

_____

_____

- -

_____

_____

- -

_____

_____

- -

_____

_____

- -

_____

_____

- -

_____

Write Like a Reporter
Informative/Explanatory

> **Student Prompt, p. 42** Look at pages 4–5 in *Flowers*. Tell why flowers are important. Write what you learned.

Writing to Sources Read pp. 4–5 of *Flowers* aloud. Discuss with children why flowers are important to plants and record children's responses on chart paper. (Flowers make seeds for plants. Flowers make fruits for plants.) Have children write or dictate one of the sentences. Suggest they might also like to draw a picture to show what the sentence means. Next, write *Parts of a Sunflower* as a title on chart paper and list numbers 1–5. Look at page 22 and ask children to name each part of a sunflower as they point to it in the illustration. Record each word in the list next to a number.

Children's sentences should:

- introduce a topic
- supply some facts and details about the topic using precise words in descriptions
- use evidence that supports key ideas
- demonstrate strong command of the conventions of standard written English

Ⓒ **Common Core State Standards**

Writing 2. Use a combination of drawing, dictating, and writing to compose informative/explanatory texts in which they name what they are writing about and supply some information about the topic.

Name_____

Connect the Texts

Informative/Explanatory

Student Prompt What seasons do you learn about in *Flowers* and "The Ant and the Grasshopper"? Tell about the seasons. Write a sentence about one of the seasons.

_____
- -
_____
- -
_____
- -
_____
- -
_____
- -
_____
- -
_____
- -
_____
- -
_____

Connect the Texts
Informative/Explanatory

Student Prompt, p. 44 What seasons do you learn about in *Flowers* and "The Ant and the Grasshopper"? Tell about the seasons. Write a sentence about one of the seasons.

Writing to Sources Have children look at the pictures for "The Ant and the Grasshopper" in *My Skills Buddy,* pp. 30–31. Ask them to identify the picture of winter and the picture of summer and to tell how the two seasons are different from each other. Have children review what they learned in *Flowers.* Ask them which season is shown in the *Flowers* selection. Provide the sentence frames: *In winter _____. In summer _____.* Record children's descriptions of summer and winter on chart paper. Have children choose one season pictured in the selections and write or dictate a sentence about it.

	Informative/Explanatory Writing Rubric				
Score	**Focus**	**Organization**	**Development of Evidence**	**Language and Vocabulary**	**Conventions**
4	Main idea is clearly conveyed and well supported; response is focused.	Organization is clear and effective, creating a sense of cohesion.	Evidence is relevant and thorough; includes facts and details.	Ideas are clearly and effectively conveyed, using precise language and/or domain-specific vocabulary.	Command of conventions is strongly demonstrated.
3	Main idea is clear, adequately supported; response is generally focused.	Organization is clear, though minor flaws may be present and some ideas may be disconnected.	Evidence is adequate and includes facts and details.	Ideas are adequately conveyed, using both precise and more general language; may include domain-specific vocabulary.	Command of conventions is sufficiently demonstrated.
2	Main idea is somewhat supported; lacks focus or includes unnecessary material.	Organization is inconsistent, and flaws are apparent.	Evidence is uneven or incomplete; insufficient use of facts and details.	Ideas are unevenly conveyed, using overly-simplistic language; lacks domain-specific vocabulary.	Command of conventions is uneven.
1	Response may be confusing, unfocused; main idea insufficiently supported.	Organization is poor or nonexistent.	Evidence is poor or nonexistent.	Ideas are conveyed in a vague, unclear, or confusing manner.	There is very little command of conventions.
0	The response shows no evidence of the ability to construct a coherent explanatory essay using information from sources.				

Ⓒ Common Core State Standards

Writing 2. Use a combination of drawing, dictating, and writing to compose informative/explanatory texts in which they name what they are writing about and supply some information about the topic.

Write Like a Reporter

Informative/Explanatory

Student Prompt Look at pages 10–11 in *Nature Spy*. Tell what the girl looks at closely in nature. Write about the plants and animals she sees.

_____

_____

_____

_____

_____

_____

_____

_____

_____

_____

_____

_____

_____

Write Like a Reporter
Informative/Explanatory

> **Student Prompt, p. 46** Look at pages 10–11 in *Nature Spy.* Tell what the girl looks at closely in nature. Write about the plants and animals she sees.

Writing to Sources Remind children that this story takes place outside during the daytime and that the girl likes to take a close look at things in nature. Read pp. 10–11 of *Nature Spy* aloud and have the children listen for what she finds. Discuss with children how something can look different when you look at it closely. Record children's responses on chart paper. (She sees the lines in a leaf. The leaf looks pointy. Up close, the leaf has a lot of shapes.) Make a T-chart with the headings *Plants* and *Animals*. Read the selection again and list what the girl sees in the correct column of the chart. Then have children write or dictate sentences using the sentence frames: *A _____ is an animal. A _____ is a plant.* Ask children to choose one sentence about an animal and one about a plant from the text and rewrite them.

Children's sentences should:
- introduce and focus on a topic
- supply some facts and descriptive details about the topic
- provide support for the main idea
- demonstrate strong command of the conventions of standard written English

ⓒ **Common Core State Standards**

Writing 2. Use a combination of drawing, dictating, and writing to compose informative/explanatory texts in which they name what they are writing about and supply some information about the topic.

Connect the Texts

Informative/Explanatory

Student Prompt Read *Nature Spy* and "The Three Wishes." Tell about what is real and what is make-believe. Write a sentence about something real.

_____

_____

_____

_____

_____

_____

_____

_____

_____

_____

_____

_____

_____

_____

Connect the Texts
Informative/Explanatory

> **Student Prompt, p. 48** Read *Nature Spy* and "The Three Wishes." Tell about what is real and what is make-believe. Write a sentence about something real.

Writing to Sources Have children review *Nature Spy* and tell about some things the girl sees outside. Ask them if this is a real or make-believe story. Have them give details from the selection to support their choice. Repeat the process with "The Three Wishes" in *My Skills Buddy,* pp. 50–51 (Teacher's Edition, pp. 197 and 294a). Then make a T-chart on chart paper with the headings *Real* and *Make-Believe.* Record children's responses as they tell what is real or make-believe from each selection. Have children write or dictate a sentence using the frame: *The girl sees a real _____ outside.*

Informative/Explanatory Writing Rubric					
Score	Focus	Organization	Development of Evidence	Language and Vocabulary	Conventions
4	Main idea is clearly conveyed and well supported; response is focused.	Organization is clear and effective, creating a sense of cohesion.	Evidence is relevant and thorough; includes facts and details.	Ideas are clearly and effectively conveyed, using precise language and/or domain-specific vocabulary.	Command of conventions is strongly demonstrated.
3	Main idea is clear, adequately supported; response is generally focused.	Organization is clear, though minor flaws may be present and some ideas may be disconnected.	Evidence is adequate and includes facts and details.	Ideas are adequately conveyed, using both precise and more general language; may include domain-specific vocabulary.	Command of conventions is sufficiently demonstrated.
2	Main idea is somewhat supported; lacks focus or includes unnecessary material.	Organization is inconsistent, and flaws are apparent.	Evidence is uneven or incomplete; insufficient use of facts and details.	Ideas are unevenly conveyed, using overly-simplistic language; lacks domain-specific vocabulary.	Command of conventions is uneven.
1	Response may be confusing, unfocused; main idea insufficiently supported.	Organization is poor or nonexistent.	Evidence is poor or nonexistent.	Ideas are conveyed in a vague, unclear, or confusing manner.	There is very little command of conventions.
0	The response shows no evidence of the ability to construct a coherent explanatory essay using information from sources.				

Ⓒ **Common Core State Standards**

Writing 2. Use a combination of drawing, dictating, and writing to compose informative/explanatory texts in which they name what they are writing about and supply some information about the topic.

Name_____

Write Like a Reporter
Informative/Explanatory

Student Prompt Look at pages 20–23 in *Animal Babies in Grasslands.* Tell what you learned about baby kangaroos called joeys. Write about baby animals.

_____

- -

_____

- -

_____

- -

_____

- -

_____

- -

_____

- -

_____

- -

_____

- -

_____

Connect the Texts
Informative/Explanatory

Student Prompt, p. 52 Read a selection about real things, *Animal Babies in Grasslands,* and a make-believe story, "Anansi's Hat-Shaking Dance." Tell about what is real and what is make-believe. Write a sentence about something make-believe.

Writing to Sources Have children review *Animal Babies in Grasslands* and tell the names of some animals and their mothers. Ask them if this is a real or make-believe story. Have them give details from the selection to support their choice. Repeat the process with "Anansi's Hat-Shaking Dance" (pp. 297 and 304a of the Teacher's Edition). Then make a T-chart on chart paper with the headings *Real* and *Make-Believe.* Record children's responses as they tell what is real or make-believe from each selection. Have children write or dictate a sentence that supports the fact that Anansi is make-believe by using the frame: *Anansi the spider is make-believe because real spiders cannot ____.*

Informative/Explanatory Writing Rubric				
Score	**Focus**	**Organization**	**Development of Evidence**	**Language and Vocabulary**	**Conventions**
4	Main idea is clearly conveyed and well supported; response is focused.	Organization is clear and effective, creating a sense of cohesion.	Evidence is relevant and thorough; includes facts and details.	Ideas are clearly and effectively conveyed, using precise language and/or domain-specific vocabulary.	Command of conventions is strongly demonstrated.
3	Main idea is clear, adequately supported; response is generally focused.	Organization is clear, though minor flaws may be present and some ideas may be disconnected.	Evidence is adequate and includes facts and details.	Ideas are adequately conveyed, using both precise and more general language; may include domain-specific vocabulary.	Command of conventions is sufficiently demonstrated.
2	Main idea is somewhat supported; lacks focus or includes unnecessary material.	Organization is inconsistent, and flaws are apparent.	Evidence is uneven or incomplete; insufficient use of facts and details.	Ideas are unevenly conveyed, using overly-simplistic language; lacks domain-specific vocabulary.	Command of conventions is uneven.
1	Response may be confusing, unfocused; main idea insufficiently supported.	Organization is poor or nonexistent.	Evidence is poor or nonexistent.	Ideas are conveyed in a vague, unclear, or confusing manner.	There is very little command of conventions.
0	The response shows no evidence of the ability to construct a coherent explanatory essay using information from sources.				

© Common Core State Standards

Writing 2. Use a combination of drawing, dictating, and writing to compose informative/explanatory texts in which they name what they are writing about and supply some information about the topic.

Name_____

Write Like a Reporter
Informative/Explanatory

Student Prompt Look at pages 30–31 in *Bear Snores On.* Name ways that Bear acts like a make-believe bear when he wakes up. Write ways that Bear acts like a real bear.

_____

- -

_____

- -

_____

- -

_____

- -

_____

- -

_____

- -

_____

- -

_____

- -

_____

Write Like a Reporter
Informative/Explanatory

> **Student Prompt, p. 54** Look at pages 30–31 in *Bear Snores On.* Name ways that Bear acts like a make-believe bear when he wakes up. Write ways that Bear acts like a real bear.

Writing to Sources Remind children that Bear is sleeping when the other animals have a party in the cave. Read pp. 30–31 of *Bear Snores On* aloud. Discuss with children how Bear acts like a make-believe bear. (He cries. He whimpers. He feels sad. Real animals don't do these things.) Now look at pp. 28–29 and list all the ways that Bear acts like a real bear. (He gnarls, snarls, roars, rumbles, jumps, stomps, growls, and grumbles.) Allow volunteers to act out the verbs. Have children write or dictate a sentence using one of these verbs and the sentence frame: *Bear acts like a real bear when he _____.*

Children's sentences should:
- introduce and focus on a topic
- supply supporting details using precise words about the topic
- provide a sense of closure
- demonstrate strong command of the conventions of standard written English

---

Ⓒ **Common Core State Standards**

Writing 2. Use a combination of drawing, dictating, and writing to compose informative/explanatory texts in which they name what they are writing about and supply some information about the topic.

Connect the Texts
Informative/Explanatory

> **Student Prompt** Read two selections that rhyme, *Bear Snores On* and "Rock-a-Bye, Baby." List the rhyming words. Which selection is a lullaby? How do you know?

_____

_____

_____

_____

_____

_____

_____

_____

_____

_____

_____

_____

_____

_____

Connect the Texts
Informative/Explanatory

Student Prompt, p. 56 Read two selections that rhyme, *Bear Snores On* and "Rock-a-Bye, Baby." List the rhyming words. Which selection is a lullaby? How do you know?

Writing to Sources Read aloud "Rock-a-Bye, Baby" (on page 399 of the Teacher's Edition), emphasizing the rhyming words. List them on chart paper as children name them. Review with children how this is a lullaby, a soothing song with rhyming words that is meant to help babies fall asleep. Then read aloud pp. 5–7 from *Bear Snores On.* Write the rhyming words from those pages on chart paper as children suggest them. Look at pp. 18–19 in *Bear Snores On* with children. Ask a volunteer to identify the words in all uppercase letters. Point out how both selections have rhyming words. Then ask children to write or dictate a sentence explaining if *Bear Snores* On is a lullaby or not.

	Informative/Explanatory Writing Rubric				
Score	Focus	Organization	Development of Evidence	Language and Vocabulary	Conventions
4	Main idea is clearly conveyed and well supported; response is focused.	Organization is clear and effective, creating a sense of cohesion.	Evidence is relevant and thorough; includes facts and details.	Ideas are clearly and effectively conveyed, using precise language and/or domain-specific vocabulary.	Command of conventions is strongly demonstrated.
3	Main idea is clear, adequately supported; response is generally focused.	Organization is clear, though minor flaws may be present and some ideas may be disconnected.	Evidence is adequate and includes facts and details.	Ideas are adequately conveyed, using both precise and more general language; may include domain-specific vocabulary.	Command of conventions is sufficiently demonstrated.
2	Main idea is somewhat supported; lacks focus or includes unnecessary material.	Organization is inconsistent, and flaws are apparent.	Evidence is uneven or incomplete; insufficient use of facts and details.	Ideas are unevenly conveyed, using overly-simplistic language; lacks domain-specific vocabulary.	Command of conventions is uneven.
1	Response may be confusing, unfocused; main idea insufficiently supported.	Organization is poor or nonexistent.	Evidence is poor or nonexistent.	Ideas are conveyed in a vague, unclear, or confusing manner.	There is very little command of conventions.
0	The response shows no evidence of the ability to construct a coherent explanatory essay using information from sources.				

© Common Core State Standards

Writing 2. Use a combination of drawing, dictating, and writing to compose informative/explanatory texts in which they name what they are writing about and supply some information about the topic.

Write Like a Reporter

Informative/Explanatory

Student Prompt Look at pages 16–17 in *A Bed for the Winter.* Tell why the dormouse does not want to sleep in the burrow with the rabbits. Write one of the reasons.

_____

_____

_____

_____

_____

_____

_____

_____

_____

_____

Write Like a Reporter
Informative/Explanatory

> **Student Prompt, p. 58** Look at pages 16–17 in *A Bed for the Winter.* Tell why the dormouse does not want to sleep in the burrow with the rabbits. Write one of the reasons.

Writing to Sources Remind children that the dormouse is looking for a home for the winter. Read pp. 16–17 of *A Bed for the Winter* aloud. Discuss with children why the rabbit's home is not a good home for the dormouse. Record children's responses on chart paper. (There are too many rabbits. There is no room for the dormouse.) Then have children write or dictate their own sentence using the sentence frame: *The dormouse does not want to sleep in the burrow because ____.*

Children's sentences should:
- identify and introduce a topic
- supply some facts and supporting details about the topic
- draw conclusions and clarify ideas using evidence from the text
- demonstrate strong command of the conventions of standard written English

© **Common Core State Standards**

Writing 2. Use a combination of drawing, dictating, and writing to compose informative/explanatory texts in which they name what they are writing about and supply some information about the topic.

Connect the Texts

Informative/Explanatory

Student Prompt There are many animals in *A Bed for the Winter* and "The House That Jack Built." List the animals in each selection. Write a sentence about one of the animals.

_____

_____

_____

_____

_____

_____

_____

_____

_____

_____

_____

_____

_____

_____

Connect the Texts
Informative/Explanatory

Student Prompt, p. 60 There are many animals in *A Bed for the Winter* and "The House That Jack Built." List the animals in each selection. Write a sentence about one of the animals.

Writing to Sources Review *A Bed for the Winter.* Look through the book page by page and record each animal and where it lives in a T-chart with the headings *Animal* and *Home*. Discuss how this is a book about real animals with photographs of each animal and its home. Use this sentence frame and have children write or dictate a sentence for each animal: *The _____ sleeps _____.* Then read aloud the nursery rhyme "The House That Jack Built" (Teacher's Edition, pp. 499 and 506a) as children look at the illustrations on pp. 110–111 in *My Skills Buddy.* Create a list on chart paper of the animals and have children identify each one in the pictures. Have children discuss the last picture and finish this sentence frame: *The animals do not sleep in the _____.*

		Informative/Explanatory Writing Rubric			
Score	**Focus**	**Organization**	**Development of Evidence**	**Language and Vocabulary**	**Conventions**
4	Main idea is clearly conveyed and well supported; response is focused.	Organization is clear and effective, creating a sense of cohesion.	Evidence is relevant and thorough; includes facts and details.	Ideas are clearly and effectively conveyed, using precise language and/or domain-specific vocabulary.	Command of conventions is strongly demonstrated.
3	Main idea is clear, adequately supported; response is generally focused.	Organization is clear, though minor flaws may be present and some ideas may be disconnected.	Evidence is adequate and includes facts and details.	Ideas are adequately conveyed, using both precise and more general language; may include domain-specific vocabulary.	Command of conventions is sufficiently demonstrated.
2	Main idea is somewhat supported; lacks focus or includes unnecessary material.	Organization is inconsistent, and flaws are apparent.	Evidence is uneven or incomplete; insufficient use of facts and details.	Ideas are unevenly conveyed, using overly-simplistic language; lacks domain-specific vocabulary.	Command of conventions is uneven.
1	Response may be confusing, unfocused; main idea insufficiently supported.	Organization is poor or nonexistent.	Evidence is poor or nonexistent.	Ideas are conveyed in a vague, unclear, or confusing manner.	There is very little command of conventions.
0	The response shows no evidence of the ability to construct a coherent explanatory essay using information from sources.				

© Common Core State Standards

Writing 2. Use a combination of drawing, dictating, and writing to compose informative/explanatory texts in which they name what they are writing about and supply some information about the topic.

Name_____

Write Like a Reporter
Informative/Explanatory

Student Prompt Look at pages 7–11 in *Jack and the Beanstalk*. Tell what Jack took from the ogre's house. Write about one thing Jack took.

_____

_____

_____

_____

_____

_____

_____

_____

_____

_____

_____

_____

Write Like a Reporter
Informative/Explanatory

> **Student Prompt, p. 62** Look at pages 7–11 in *Jack and the Beanstalk*. Tell what Jack took from the ogre's house. Write about one thing Jack took.

Writing to Sources Remind children that Jack took things from the ogre's house. Read pp. 7–11 of *Jack and the Beanstalk* aloud. Discuss with children each item that Jack took from the ogre's house. Record their responses on chart paper. (magic hen that lays gold eggs, bags of gold, golden harp) Have children write or dictate their own sentence using this sentence frame: *Jack took _____ from the ogre's house.*

Children's sentences should:

- identify and focus on a topic
- supply supporting details using precise words about the topic
- use evidence from the text to support and clarify key ideas
- demonstrate strong command of the conventions of standard written English

Ⓒ **Common Core State Standards**

Writing 2. Use a combination of drawing, dictating, and writing to compose informative/explanatory texts in which they name what they are writing about and supply some information about the topic.

Connect the Texts

Informative/Explanatory

Student Prompt Read about make-believe and real plants in *Jack and the Beanstalk* and "Parts of a Plant." Tell the parts of a real plant. Draw a magic beanstalk and label its parts.

_____

_____

_____

_____

_____

_____

_____

_____

_____

Connect the Texts
Informative/Explanatory

Student Prompt, p. 64 Read about make-believe and real plants in *Jack and the Beanstalk* and "Parts of a Plant." Tell the parts of a real plant. Draw a magic beanstalk and label its parts.

Writing to Sources Review how in *Jack and the Beanstalk* the magic beans grew into a very tall stalk that reached the clouds. Look at the illustration for "Parts of a Plant" in *My Skills Buddy,* pp. 130–131. Write *Parts of a Plant* as a title on chart paper and list numbers 1–4. Have children name each part of a plant as they point to it in the illustration. Record each word in the list next to a number. Then have children draw the magic beans and beanstalk from *Jack and the Beanstalk* and use the same words to label their picture.

		Informative/Explanatory Writing Rubric			
Score	Focus	Organization	Development of Evidence	Language and Vocabulary	Conventions
4	Main idea is clearly conveyed and well supported; response is focused.	Organization is clear and effective, creating a sense of cohesion.	Evidence is relevant and thorough; includes facts and details.	Ideas are clearly and effectively conveyed, using precise language and/or domain-specific vocabulary.	Command of conventions is strongly demonstrated.
3	Main idea is clear, adequately supported; response is generally focused.	Organization is clear, though minor flaws may be present and some ideas may be disconnected.	Evidence is adequate and includes facts and details.	Ideas are adequately conveyed, using both precise and more general language; may include domain-specific vocabulary.	Command of conventions is sufficiently demonstrated.
2	Main idea is somewhat supported; lacks focus or includes unnecessary material.	Organization is inconsistent, and flaws are apparent.	Evidence is uneven or incomplete; insufficient use of facts and details.	Ideas are unevenly conveyed, using overly-simplistic language; lacks domain-specific vocabulary.	Command of conventions is uneven.
1	Response may be confusing, unfocused; main idea insufficiently supported.	Organization is poor or nonexistent.	Evidence is poor or nonexistent.	Ideas are conveyed in a vague, unclear, or confusing manner.	There is very little command of conventions.
0	The response shows no evidence of the ability to construct a coherent explanatory essay using information from sources.				

Ⓒ Common Core State Standards

Writing 2. Use a combination of drawing, dictating, and writing to compose informative/explanatory texts in which they name what they are writing about and supply some information about the topic.

Prove It!
Expository Paragraph

Plants

Expository Paragraph

In this unit, children have read examples of informative/explanatory writing and have had the opportunity to write in this mode. Remind children of texts and writing tasks (such as Write Like a Reporter) in which they have encountered and practiced informative/explanatory writing.

Key Features of an Expository Paragraph
- tells about real people, places, or things
- uses facts to tell about the main idea
- uses specific words to make facts clear
- develops the topic with facts, definitions, and details

Writing Task Overview

Each unit writing task provides children with an opportunity to write using information from a selection they are reading. To successfully complete the task, children must understand and interpret the selection and create their own response.

Plants

Part 1: Children will reread a selection identified from this unit. They will then respond to the selection and discuss their written response with partners.

Part 2: Children will work individually to plan, write, and revise their own expository paragraph.

Scorable Products: evidence-based short response, expository paragraph

Plants: Writing Task – Short Response

Teacher Directions:

1. Introduce the Source Reread the following Big Book selection:

Flowers

Explain to children that they will use the words and illustrations in the book to respond. Tell children that they will also write their own expository paragraphs that use information from the text.

2. Have children draw a picture of one plant in *Flowers*.

3. Using evidence from the text, have children write or dictate a sentence that gives information about the plant they have chosen.

© Common Core State Standards

Writing 2. Use a combination of drawing, dictating, and writing to compose informative/explanatory texts in which they name what they are writing about and supply some information about the topic.

Scoring Information

Use the following 2-point scoring rubric to evaluate children's answers to the evidence-based short response.

	Analysis Rubric
2	The response: • demonstrates the ability to analyze facts and details in the text in order to give information about a plant • includes specific details that make reference to the text
1	The response: • demonstrates a limited ability to analyze facts and details in the text in order to give information about a plant • includes some details that make reference to the text
0	A response receives no credit if it demonstrates no ability to analyze information or includes no relevant details from the text.

Ⓒ **Common Core State Standards**

Writing 2. Use a combination of drawing, dictating, and writing to compose informative/explanatory texts in which they name what they are writing about and supply some information about the topic.

Plants

Writing Task – Short Response

Draw a picture of a plant from *Flowers*.

Name _____

Write a sentence telling about the plant.

_____

- -

_____

- -

_____

- -

_____

- -

_____

- -

_____

- -

_____

- -

_____

- -

_____

- -

_____

- -

Plants: Writing Task – Expository Paragraph

Teacher Directions:

1. Have children draw a picture of a plant from the selection *Flowers*.

2. Have children write or dictate a short paragraph that gives information about the plant. Tell them to include facts from the selection.

3. Scoring Information Use the scoring rubric on the next page to evaluate children's expository paragraphs.

© Common Core State Standards

Writing 2. Use a combination of drawing, dictating, and writing to compose informative/explanatory texts in which they name what they are writing about and supply some information about the topic.

Informative/Explanatory Writing Rubric

Score	Focus	Organization	Development of Evidence	Language and Vocabulary	Conventions
4	Main idea is clearly stated.	Organization is clear.	Evidence includes many facts and details.	Ideas are clearly and effectively conveyed, using precise language.	Command of conventions is strongly demonstrated.
3	Main idea is adequately stated.	Organization is clear, though minor flaws may be present.	Evidence includes some facts and details.	Ideas are adequately conveyed, using precise language.	Command of conventions is sufficiently demonstrated.
2	Main idea is somewhat stated.	Organization is inconsistent.	Evidence has insufficient use of facts or details.	Ideas are unevenly conveyed, using overly-simplistic language.	Command of conventions is uneven.
1	Response may be unfocused.	Organization is poor or nonexistent.	Evidence is poor or nonexistent.	Ideas are conveyed in a vague or confusing manner.	There is very little command of conventions.
0	The response shows no evidence of the ability to construct a coherent informative/explanatory paragraph using information from sources.				

ⓒ Common Core State Standards

Writing 2. Use a combination of drawing, dictating, and writing to compose informative/explanatory texts in which they name what they are writing about and supply some information about the topic.

Plants

Writing Task – Expository Paragraph

Expository Paragraph Prompt

Draw a picture of a plant from *Flowers*. Write a short paragraph that tells about the plant. Your paragraph should tell facts about the flower.

Plants: Writing Task – Expository Paragraph

Teacher Directions:

1. Publish Explain to children that publishing their writing is the last step in the writing process. If time permits, have children review one another's paragraphs and incorporate any comments their classmates have. Discuss different ways technology can be used to publish writing.

2. Present Children will now have the option to present their expository paragraphs. Have children tell about their paragraphs in front of the class. Use the list below to offer children some tips on listening and speaking.

While Listening to a Classmate...
- Think about what the speaker is saying.
- Raise your hand to ask a question.

While Speaking to Classmates...
- Stay on topic.
- Speak clearly.

Things to Do Together...
- Follow agreed-upon discussion rules.
- Ask and answer questions.

© Common Core State Standards

Writing 2. Use a combination of drawing, dictating, and writing to compose informative/explanatory texts in which they name what they are writing about and supply some information about the topic.

Unit 3 Changes All Around Us

Writing Focus: Argument

Write Like a Reporter
Argument

> **Student Prompt** Look at pp. 14–21 in *Little Panda*. What things does Hua Mei do? Write about your favorite activity.

_____
_____
_____
_____
_____
_____
_____
_____
_____
_____
_____
_____
_____
_____
_____
_____
_____

Write Like a Reporter
Argument

Student Prompt, p. 78 Look at pp. 14–21 in *Little Panda.* What things does Hua Mei do? Write about your favorite activity.

Writing to Sources Have children look at the story *Little Panda.* Reread pp. 16–29 of *Little Panda.* Next have children look through the story and choose the pages that show their favorite activity that Hua Mei is doing. Have them explain why it is their favorite and record their responses in complete sentences on chart paper. Have children write (or copy from the chart paper) the sentence that gives their opinion about a favorite activity. Remind them to use details and evidence from the selection to support their opinion.

Children's sentences should:

- introduce the topic
- state their opinion about a favorite activity
- supply a reason for the opinion
- demonstrate strong command of the conventions of standard written English

---

ⓒ Common Core State Standards

Writing 1. Use a combination of drawing, dictating, and writing to compose opinion pieces in which they tell a reader the topic or the name of the book they are writing about and state an opinion or preference about the topic or book (e.g., *My favorite book is . . .*).

Connect the Texts

Argument

> **Student Prompt** Read about a baby panda in *Little Panda.* Read the poems "Star Light, Star Bright" and "Twinkle, Twinkle, Little Star." Tell which selection is your favorite. Write a sentence about your favorite.

_____

_ _

_____

_ _

_____

_ _

_____

_ _

_____

_ _

_____

_ _

_____

Connect the Texts
Argument

> **Student Prompt, p. 80** Read about a baby panda in *Little Panda*.
> Read the poems "Star Light, Star Bright" and "Twinkle, Twinkle, Little Star."
> Tell which selection is your favorite. Write a sentence about your favorite.

Writing to Sources Read aloud "Star Light, Star Bright" and "Twinkle, Twinkle, Little Star" in the Teacher's Edition on p. 99. Be sure to emphasize the rhyming words in each poem. Ask children to complete this sentence frame: *My favorite poem is* ____. Discuss how *Little Panda* tells about a real animal and her experiences. Then read pp. 16–17 in *Little Panda* aloud to children. Ask children which selection they enjoyed listening to more—the poems or the information about Hua Mei. Have them complete the sentence frame: *I liked* ____ *because* ____. Remind them to give reasons to support their opinion when they complete the *because* part of the sentence.

		4-point Argument Writing Rubric			
Score	**Statement of Purpose/Focus**	**Organization**	**Development of Evidence**	**Language and Vocabulary**	**Conventions**
4	Opinion is clearly conveyed and well supported; response is focused.	Organization is clear and effective, creating a sense of cohesion.	Evidence is thorough and persuasive, and includes facts and details.	Ideas are clearly and effectively conveyed, using precise language and/or domain-specific vocabulary.	Command of conventions is strongly demonstrated.
3	Opinion is clear, adequately supported; response is generally focused.	Organization is clear, though minor flaws may be present and some ideas may be disconnected.	Evidence is adequate and includes facts and details.	Ideas are adequately conveyed, using both precise and more general language; may include domain-specific vocabulary.	Command of conventions is sufficiently demonstrated.
2	Opinion is somewhat supported; response may lack focus or include unnecessary material.	Organization is inconsistent, and flaws are apparent.	Evidence is uneven or incomplete; insufficient use of facts and details.	Ideas are unevenly conveyed, using overly-simplistic language; lack of domain-specific vocabulary.	Command of conventions is uneven.
1	The response may be confusing, unfocused; opinion not sufficiently supported.	Organization is poor or nonexistent.	Evidence is poor or nonexistent.	Ideas are conveyed in a vague, unclear, or confusing manner.	There is very little command of conventions.
0	The response shows no evidence of the ability to construct a coherent opinion essay using information from sources.				

Ⓒ **Common Core State Standards**

Writing 1. Use a combination of drawing, dictating, and writing to compose opinion pieces in which they tell a reader the topic or the name of the book they are writing about and state an opinion or preference about the topic or book (e.g., *My favorite book is . . .*).

Name_____

Write Like a Reporter
Argument

Student Prompt Look at pages 24–27 in *Little Quack.* Little Quack does not want to go in the water because he is "just too scared." If you were one of the ducks in *Little Quack,* which one would you be? Write about why you chose that duck.

_____
- -
_____
- -
_____
- -
_____
- -
_____
- -
_____
- -
_____
- -
_____

Write Like a Reporter
Argument

> **Student Prompt, p. 82** Look at pages 24–27 in *Little Quack.* Little Quack does not want to go in the water because he is "just too scared." If you were one of the ducks in *Little Quack,* which one would you be? Write about why you chose that duck.

Writing to Sources Tell children to look at the story *Little Quack* and write about it. Help children remember that Little Quack is "just too scared" to go into the water. Read pp. 24–27 of *Little Quack.* Ask children which duck they would like to be. Write their responses on chart paper. Guide them to write their opinion by completing the sentence frame: *I would like to be _____ because _____.*

Children's sentences should:
- introduce the topic
- state a clear opinion
- demonstrate strong command of the conventions of standard written English

© Common Core State Standards

Writing 1. Use a combination of drawing, dictating, and writing to compose opinion pieces in which they tell a reader the topic or the name of the book they are writing about and state an opinion or preference about the topic or book (e.g., *My favorite book is . . .*).

Connect the Texts
Argument

Student Prompt Read about make-believe ducks in *Little Quack.* Listen to the fairy tale "Rumpelstiltskin." Who is your favorite character—Little Quack or Rumpelstiltskin? Why? Draw a picture of your favorite character. Write about your favorite character.

_____

_____

_____

_____

_____

_____

Connect the Texts
Argument

Student Prompt, p. 84 Read about make-believe ducks in *Little Quack*. Listen to the fairy tale "Rumpelstiltskin." Who is your favorite character—Little Quack or Rumpelstiltskin? Why? Draw a picture of your favorite character. Write about your favorite character.

Writing to Sources Review *Little Quack* and "Rumpelstiltskin" (Teacher's Edition, p. 199). Talk about the character Rumpelstiltskin and what he does. Then ask children whether or not they like him and why. Then discuss Little Quack and what children like or dislike about him. Have children write the name of the character they like best as a title and draw a picture of that character underneath. Have them finish this sentence frame and put it at the bottom of the page: *My favorite character is _____ because _____.*

		4-point Argument Writing Rubric			
Score	**Statement of Purpose/Focus**	**Organization**	**Development of Evidence**	**Language and Vocabulary**	**Conventions**
4	Opinion is clearly conveyed and well supported; response is focused.	Organization is clear and effective, creating a sense of cohesion.	Evidence is thorough and persuasive, and includes facts and details.	Ideas are clearly and effectively conveyed, using precise language and/or domain-specific vocabulary.	Command of conventions is strongly demonstrated.
3	Opinion is clear, adequately supported; response is generally focused.	Organization is clear, though minor flaws may be present and some ideas may be disconnected.	Evidence is adequate and includes facts and details.	Ideas are adequately conveyed, using both precise and more general language; may include domain-specific vocabulary.	Command of conventions is sufficiently demonstrated.
2	Opinion is somewhat supported; response may lack focus or include unnecessary material.	Organization is inconsistent, and flaws are apparent.	Evidence is uneven or incomplete; insufficient use of facts and details.	Ideas are unevenly conveyed, using overly-simplistic language; lack of domain-specific vocabulary.	Command of conventions is uneven.
1	The response may be confusing, unfocused; opinion not sufficiently supported.	Organization is poor or nonexistent.	Evidence is poor or nonexistent.	Ideas are conveyed in a vague, unclear, or confusing manner.	There is very little command of conventions.
0	The response shows no evidence of the ability to construct a coherent opinion essay using information from sources.				

Ⓒ Common Core State Standards

Writing 1. Use a combination of drawing, dictating, and writing to compose opinion pieces in which they tell a reader the topic or the name of the book they are writing about and state an opinion or preference about the topic or book (e.g., *My favorite book is . . .*).

Name_____

Write Like a Reporter
Argument

> **Student Prompt** Look at pages 18–19 in *George Washington Visits.* George Washington is leading soldiers into a battle. Do you think it was hard to be a soldier in Washington's army? Write your opinion.

_____

- -

_____

- -

_____

- -

_____

- -

_____

- -

_____

- -

_____

- -

_____

Write Like a Reporter
Argument

> **Student Prompt, p. 86** Look at pages 18–19 in *George Washington Visits*. George Washington is leading soldiers into a battle. Do you think it was hard to be a soldier in Washington's army? Write your opinion.

Writing to Sources Have children look at the story *George Washington Visits* and tell them they will be writing about it. Help children remember that Father was one of George Washington's soldiers. Read pp. 18–19 of *George Washington Visits.* Ask children to point out details in the picture that support the idea that it was hard to be a soldier. Make a list of their ideas on chart paper. Discuss with children the evidence in the illustration that supports this idea. Have children use those words to complete the sentence frame: *It was hard to be a soldier because* ____.

Children's sentences should:
- introduce the topic
- state an opinion
- use evidence from the text to support their reasons
- demonstrate strong command of the conventions of standard written English

© **Common Core State Standards**

Writing 1. Use a combination of drawing, dictating, and writing to compose opinion pieces in which they tell a reader the topic or the name of the book they are writing about and state an opinion or preference about the topic or book (e.g., *My favorite book is . . .*).

Connect the Texts

Argument

Student Prompt A father and son make a sign in *George Washington Visits.* A man and two girls conduct a science experiment in "Can Celery Sip?" Were the children in each selection having fun? Write about the two girls.

_____

_____

_____

_____

_____

_____

_____

_____

_____

_____

_____

_____

_____

_____

Connect the Texts
Argument

Student Prompt, p. 88 A father and son make a sign in *George Washington Visits.* A man and two girls conduct a science experiment in "Can Celery Sip?" Were the children in each selection having fun? Write about the two girls.

Writing to Sources Have children read p. 10 of *George Washington Visits* and look at the picture. Ask them how they think the boy feels. Explain that in the picture the boy looks sad, but the words say that he likes helping. Then direct children to look at the two girls on pp. 70–71 in *My Skills Buddy*. Have them draw conclusions as they discuss how these girls might be feeling. Write their responses on chart paper and have children complete this sentence frame on their papers: *I think the girls are having fun because _____.*

	4-point Argument Writing Rubric				
Score	**Statement of Purpose/Focus**	**Organization**	**Development of Evidence**	**Language and Vocabulary**	**Conventions**
4	Opinion is clearly conveyed and well supported; response is focused.	Organization is clear and effective, creating a sense of cohesion.	Evidence is thorough and persuasive, and includes facts and details.	Ideas are clearly and effectively conveyed, using precise language and/or domain-specific vocabulary.	Command of conventions is strongly demonstrated.
3	Opinion is clear, adequately supported; response is generally focused.	Organization is clear, though minor flaws may be present and some ideas may be disconnected.	Evidence is adequate and includes facts and details.	Ideas are adequately conveyed, using both precise and more general language; may include domain-specific vocabulary.	Command of conventions is sufficiently demonstrated.
2	Opinion is somewhat supported; response may lack focus or include unnecessary material.	Organization is inconsistent, and flaws are apparent.	Evidence is uneven or incomplete; insufficient use of facts and details.	Ideas are unevenly conveyed, using overly-simplistic language; lack of domain-specific vocabulary.	Command of conventions is uneven.
1	The response may be confusing, unfocused; opinion not sufficiently supported.	Organization is poor or nonexistent.	Evidence is poor or nonexistent.	Ideas are conveyed in a vague, unclear, or confusing manner.	There is very little command of conventions.
0	The response shows no evidence of the ability to construct a coherent opinion essay using information from sources.				

Ⓒ Common Core State Standards

Writing 1. Use a combination of drawing, dictating, and writing to compose opinion pieces in which they tell a reader the topic or the name of the book they are writing about and state an opinion or preference about the topic or book (e.g., *My favorite book is . . .*).

Name_____

Write Like a Reporter
Argument

Student Prompt Reread *Farfallina and Marcel.* Talk about ways the two animals change. Write about who changes more.

_____

_____

_____

_____

_____

_____

_____

_____

_____

_____

_____

_____

Write Like a Reporter
Argument

> **Student Prompt, p. 90** Reread *Farfallina and Marcel*. Talk about ways the two animals change. Write about who changes more.

Writing to Sources Tell children that they are going to look back at the story *Farfallina and Marcel* and are going to write about it. Help children remember that when Farfallina and Marcel meet again, they don't recognize each other. Tell children to listen for the reasons why they don't recognize each other. First have children look at pp. 10–11 and then read pp. 22–25 of *Farfallina and Marcel* aloud. Discuss with children why the friends don't recognize each other and record their responses on chart paper. Review the list they created of changes to each animal. Have children look at these details from the story and ask children which character changed more. Have children choose the character they think changed more and finish this sentence frame: *I think that _____ changed more than _____ because _____.*

Children's sentences should:

- introduce the topic
- state an opinion
- demonstrate strong command of the conventions of standard written English

Ⓒ **Common Core State Standards**

Writing 1. Use a combination of drawing, dictating, and writing to compose opinion pieces in which they tell a reader the topic or the name of the book they are writing about and state an opinion or preference about the topic or book (e.g., *My favorite book is . . .*).

Connect the Texts

Argument

> **Student Prompt** In *Farfallina and Marcel,* two animals are good friends. In "The Mice and the Cat" the animals do not get along. Which story is more like real life? Write about your ideas.

_____

_____

_____

_____

_____

_____

_____

_____

_____

_____

Connect the Texts
Argument

Student Prompt, p. 92 In *Farfallina and Marcel,* two animals are good friends. In "The Mice and the Cat" the animals do not get along. Which story is more like real life? Write about your ideas.

Writing to Sources Reread *Farfallina and Marcel* and "The Mice and the Cat" on page 397 of the Teacher's Edition with children. Point out that a caterpillar and a bird become good friends at the beginning of *Farfallina and Marcel.* Even when the caterpillar becomes a butterfly, the animals are still able to be friends. Friendship between animals does not happen in "The Mice and the Cat." The cat sneaks up on the mice, chases them, and tries to eat them. Ask children to think about animals in real life. Even though these are make-believe stories, which animals act more like real animals in how they get along? Then have them write their opinion by completing this sentence frame: *I think the animals in _____ are more like animals in real life because _____.*

4-point Argument Writing Rubric					
Score	Statement of Purpose/Focus	Organization	Development of Evidence	Language and Vocabulary	Conventions
4	Opinion is clearly conveyed and well supported; response is focused.	Organization is clear and effective, creating a sense of cohesion.	Evidence is thorough and persuasive, and includes facts and details.	Ideas are clearly and effectively conveyed, using precise language and/or domain-specific vocabulary.	Command of conventions is strongly demonstrated.
3	Opinion is clear, adequately supported; response is generally focused.	Organization is clear, though minor flaws may be present and some ideas may be disconnected.	Evidence is adequate and includes facts and details.	Ideas are adequately conveyed, using both precise and more general language; may include domain-specific vocabulary.	Command of conventions is sufficiently demonstrated.
2	Opinion is somewhat supported; response may lack focus or include unnecessary material.	Organization is inconsistent, and flaws are apparent.	Evidence is uneven or incomplete; insufficient use of facts and details.	Ideas are unevenly conveyed, using overly-simplistic language; lack of domain-specific vocabulary.	Command of conventions is uneven.
1	The response may be confusing, unfocused; opinion not sufficiently supported.	Organization is poor or nonexistent.	Evidence is poor or nonexistent.	Ideas are conveyed in a vague, unclear, or confusing manner.	There is very little command of conventions.
0	The response shows no evidence of the ability to construct a coherent opinion essay using information from sources.				

© Common Core State Standards

Writing 1. Use a combination of drawing, dictating, and writing to compose opinion pieces in which they tell a reader the topic or the name of the book they are writing about and state an opinion or preference about the topic or book (e.g., *My favorite book is . . .*).

Name_____

Write Like a Reporter
Argument

Student Prompt Look at pp. 12–13 in *Then and Now.* Think about children getting to school in the past and now. Write about the way you think is faster.

_____

- - - - - - - - - - - - - - - - - - - -

_____

- - - - - - - - - - - - - - - - - - - -

_____

- - - - - - - - - - - - - - - - - - - -

_____

- - - - - - - - - - - - - - - - - - - -

_____

- - - - - - - - - - - - - - - - - - - -

_____

- - - - - - - - - - - - - - - - - - - -

_____

- - - - - - - - - - - - - - - - - - - -

_____

- - - - - - - - - - - - - - - - - - - -

Write Like a Reporter

Argument

> **Student Prompt, p. 94** Look at pp. 12–13 in *Then and Now*. Think about children getting to school in the past and now. Write about the way you think is faster.

Writing to Sources Remind children that we know that many things have changed from long ago. Tell children to listen to how getting to school has changed. Read pp. 12–13 of *Then and Now*. Discuss which way children think is faster to get to school. Create a list of ways children can get to school today. (riding on a bus; riding in cars; riding a bicycle; walking) Then talk about getting to school in a buggy pulled by a horse. Have children draw a picture of the way they think is faster to get to school. Have them complete this sentence frame and use it to label their picture: *I think that _____ to school is faster because _____.*

Children's sentences should:

- introduce the topic
- state an opinion clearly
- demonstrate strong command of the conventions of standard written English

© **Common Core State Standards**

Writing 1. Use a combination of drawing, dictating, and writing to compose opinion pieces in which they tell a reader the topic or the name of the book they are writing about and state an opinion or preference about the topic or book (e.g., *My favorite book is . . .*).

Connect the Texts

Argument

Student Prompt Read about how things have changed in *Then and Now.* Listen to a story about a coyote that brings fire to people in "How Coyote Helped People." Think about which selection you enjoyed listening to. Write a sentence about it.

_____

_____

_____

_____

_____

_____

_____

_____

_____

_____

Connect the Texts
Argument

Student Prompt, p. 96 Read about how things have changed in *Then and Now*. Listen to a story about a coyote that brings fire to people in "How Coyote Helped People." Think about which selection you enjoyed listening to. Write a sentence about it.

Writing to Sources Read aloud pp. 6–9 in *Then and Now*. Then reread the folk tale "How Coyote Helped People" on page 495 of the Teacher's Edition. Ask children which selection they enjoyed listening to more—the selection about how things have changed or the story of why coyotes have white tails. Have them explain why they enjoyed listening to it and record their responses in complete sentences on chart paper. Have children write a new sentence or copy a sentence from the chart paper that states their opinion about their favorite selection.

	4-point Argument Writing Rubric				
Score	**Statement of Purpose/Focus**	**Organization**	**Development of Evidence**	**Language and Vocabulary**	**Conventions**
4	Opinion is clearly conveyed and well supported; response is focused.	Organization is clear and effective, creating a sense of cohesion.	Evidence is thorough and persuasive, and includes facts and details.	Ideas are clearly and effectively conveyed, using precise language and/or domain-specific vocabulary.	Command of conventions is strongly demonstrated.
3	Opinion is clear, adequately supported; response is generally focused.	Organization is clear, though minor flaws may be present and some ideas may be disconnected.	Evidence is adequate and includes facts and details.	Ideas are adequately conveyed, using both precise and more general language; may include domain-specific vocabulary.	Command of conventions is sufficiently demonstrated.
2	Opinion is somewhat supported; response may lack focus or include unnecessary material.	Organization is inconsistent, and flaws are apparent.	Evidence is uneven or incomplete; insufficient use of facts and details.	Ideas are unevenly conveyed, using overly-simplistic language; lack of domain-specific vocabulary.	Command of conventions is uneven.
1	The response may be confusing, unfocused; opinion not sufficiently supported.	Organization is poor or nonexistent.	Evidence is poor or nonexistent.	Ideas are conveyed in a vague, unclear, or confusing manner.	There is very little command of conventions.
0	The response shows no evidence of the ability to construct a coherent opinion essay using information from sources.				

© Common Core State Standards

Writing 1. Use a combination of drawing, dictating, and writing to compose opinion pieces in which they tell a reader the topic or the name of the book they are writing about and state an opinion or preference about the topic or book (e.g., *My favorite book is . . .*).

Write Like a Reporter
Argument

Student Prompt Read *The Lion and the Mouse.* Talk about the two characters—the lion and the mouse. Write about your favorite character. Tell why that character is your favorite.

_____

_____

_____

_____

_____

_____

_____

_____

_____

_____

_____

_____

Write Like a Reporter
Argument

> **Student Prompt, p. 98** Read *The Lion and the Mouse*. Talk about the two characters—the lion and the mouse. Write about your favorite character. Tell why that character is your favorite.

Writing to Sources Reread pp. 10–13 of *The Lion and the Mouse*. Talk about what the lion says to the mouse and what the lion does. Then reread pp. 22–25 and talk about the mouse's words and actions. Write children's responses on chart paper under the headings *Lion* and *Mouse*. Then ask children to think about which character is their favorite. Have them use words and ideas from the chart paper to complete the sentence frame: *My favorite character is _____ because he (she) _____.* Remind them to give reasons to support their opinion when they complete the *because* part of the sentence.

Children's sentences should:
- introduce the topic of favorite character
- state an opinion
- supply a reason for the opinion
- demonstrate strong command of the conventions of standard written English

© **Common Core State Standards**

Writing 1. Use a combination of drawing, dictating, and writing to compose opinion pieces in which they tell a reader the topic or the name of the book they are writing about and state an opinion or preference about the topic or book (e.g., *My favorite book is . . .*).

Connect the Texts

Argument

> **Student Prompt** Read about how a mouse helps a lion in *The Lion and the Mouse*. Listen to an expository text about real lions in "Lions." Think about a real mouse and a real lion. Write your opinion: Can a real mouse help a real lion?

_____

- -

_____

- -

_____

- -

_____

- -

_____

- -

_____

- -

_____

- -

_____

- -

_____

Connect the Texts
Argument

> **Student Prompt, p. 100** Read about how a mouse helps a lion in *The Lion and the Mouse*. Listen to an expository text about real lions in "Lions." Think about a real mouse and a real lion. Write your opinion: Can a real mouse help a real lion?

Writing to Sources Review *The Lion and the Mouse* and "Lions" on page 593 of the Teacher's Edition with children. Remind them that one selection is a make-believe story and the other gives facts about real lions. Challenge children to discuss the possibility of a real mouse helping a real lion. Have them use details from "Lions" to support their opinions. Record their ideas on chart paper. Then have them complete this sentence frame: *I think a real mouse (can/cannot) help a real lion because* _____.

\multicolumn{6}{c}{4-point Argument Writing Rubric}					
Score	Statement of Purpose/Focus	Organization	Development of Evidence	Language and Vocabulary	Conventions
4	Opinion is clearly conveyed and well supported; response is focused.	Organization is clear and effective, creating a sense of cohesion.	Evidence is thorough and persuasive, and includes facts and details.	Ideas are clearly and effectively conveyed, using precise language and/or domain-specific vocabulary.	Command of conventions is strongly demonstrated.
3	Opinion is clear, adequately supported; response is generally focused.	Organization is clear, though minor flaws may be present and some ideas may be disconnected.	Evidence is adequate and includes facts and details.	Ideas are adequately conveyed, using both precise and more general language; may include domain-specific vocabulary.	Command of conventions is sufficiently demonstrated.
2	Opinion is somewhat supported; response may lack focus or include unnecessary material.	Organization is inconsistent, and flaws are apparent.	Evidence is uneven or incomplete; insufficient use of facts and details.	Ideas are unevenly conveyed, using overly-simplistic language; lack of domain-specific vocabulary.	Command of conventions is uneven.
1	The response may be confusing, unfocused; opinion not sufficiently supported.	Organization is poor or nonexistent.	Evidence is poor or nonexistent.	Ideas are conveyed in a vague, unclear, or confusing manner.	There is very little command of conventions.
0	\multicolumn{5}{l}{The response shows no evidence of the ability to construct a coherent opinion essay using information from sources.}				

© Common Core State Standards

Writing 1. Use a combination of drawing, dictating, and writing to compose opinion pieces in which they tell a reader the topic or the name of the book they are writing about and state an opinion or preference about the topic or book (e.g., *My favorite book is . . .*).

Prove It!
Opinion Paragraph

Academic Vocabulary

An opinion paragraph is a type of argument or opinion writing. In opinion writing, the writer tells what he or she thinks about a topic, issue, or text.

ELL

Introduce Genre Write the word *opinion* on the board. Explain that this word is used to identify writing that tells what the writer thinks about something. Discuss with children the key features of an opinion paragraph that appear on this page.

My Favorite Character

Opinion Paragraph

In this unit, children have read examples of argument writing and have had the opportunity to write in this mode. Remind children of texts and writing tasks (such as Write Like a Reporter) in which they have encountered and practiced argument writing.

Key Features of an Opinion Paragraph
- states the writer's opinion on a topic
- supports the opinion with reasons
- provides facts and details from the source
- provides a concluding statement that summarizes the writer's main point

Writing Task Overview

Each unit writing task provides children with an opportunity to write using information from a selection they are reading. To successfully complete the task, children must understand and interpret the selection and create their own written response.

My Favorite Character

Part 1: Children will reread a selection identified from this unit. They will then respond to the selection and discuss their written response with partners.

Part 2: Children will work individually to plan, write, and revise their own opinion paragraph.

Scorable Products: evidence-based short response, opinion paragraph

My Favorite Character: Writing Task – Short Response

Teacher Directions:

1. Introduce the Source Reread the following Big Book selection:

Farfallina and Marcel

Explain to children that they will use the words and illustrations in the book to respond. Tell children that they will also write their own opinion paragraphs that use information from the text.

2. Have children draw a picture of one character in *Farfallina and Marcel*.

3. Using evidence from the text, have children write or dictate a description of the character they have chosen. Tell them to include a reason they like the character.

ⓒ Common Core State Standards

Writing 1. Use a combination of drawing, dictating, and writing to compose opinion pieces in which they tell a reader the topic or the name of the book they are writing about and state an opinion or preference about the topic or book (e.g., *My favorite book is …*)

Scoring Information

Use the following 2-point scoring rubric to evaluate children's answers to the evidence-based short response.

	Evaluation Rubric
2	The response: • demonstrates the ability to evaluate text and form an opinion about a character • includes specific details that make reference to the text
1	The response: • demonstrates a limited ability to evaluate text and form an opinion about a character • includes some details that make reference to the text
0	A response gets no credit if it shows no ability to evaluate text or includes no relevant details from the text.

© Common Core State Standards

Writing 1. Use a combination of drawing, dictating, and writing to compose opinion pieces in which they tell a reader the topic or the name of the book they are writing about and state an opinion or preference about the topic or book (e.g., *My favorite book is …*)

My Favorite Character
Writing Task – Short Response

Draw a picture of Farfallina or Marcel.

Name _____

Write a sentence about the character.
Tell why you like the character.

_____
- -
_____
- -
_____
- -
_____
- -
_____
- -
_____
- -
_____
- -
_____
- -
_____

My Favorite Character: Writing Task – Opinion Paragraph

Teacher Directions:

1. Have children draw a picture of the two main characters in the story *Farfallina and Marcel.*

2. Have children write or dictate a short paragraph that gives their opinion about the characters. Have them tell which character is their favorite and include reasons why.

3. Scoring Information Use the scoring rubric on the next page to evaluate children's opinion paragraphs.

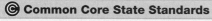 **Common Core State Standards**

Writing 1. Use a combination of drawing, dictating, and writing to compose opinion pieces in which they tell a reader the topic or the name of the book they are writing about and state an opinion or preference about the topic or book (e.g., *My favorite book is* …)

Argument Writing Rubric

Score	Statement of Purpose/Focus	Organization	Development of Evidence	Language and Vocabulary	Conventions
4	Paragraph clearly gives an opinion of the characters in the selection.	Organization includes a clear opinion with a strong reason.	Evidence includes sufficient facts and details.	Persuasive words are effectively used.	Use of conventions is clearly shown.
3	Paragraph adequately gives an opinion of the characters in the selection.	Organization includes an opinion and a reason.	Evidence includes some facts and details.	Persuasive words are used.	Use of conventions is somewhat shown.
2	Paragraph somewhat gives an opinion of the characters in the selection.	Organization includes an opinion but no reason.	Evidence does not include facts and details.	Few persuasive words are used.	Use of conventions is uneven.
1	Paragraph does not include a stated opinion.	Organization lacks opinion, reasons, and conclusion.	Evidence is poor or nonexistent.	There is little or no use of persuasive words.	There is very little correct use of conventions.
0	The response shows no evidence of the ability to construct a coherent opinion paragraph using information from sources.				

© Common Core State Standards

Writing 1. Use a combination of drawing, dictating, and writing to compose opinion pieces in which they tell a reader the topic or the name of the book they are writing about and state an opinion or preference about the topic or book (e.g., *My favorite book is …*)

My Favorite Character
Writing Task – Opinion Paragraph

Opinion Paragraph Prompt

Draw a picture of Farfallina and Marcel. Which character is your favorite? Write a paragraph that tells why.

My Favorite Character: Writing Task – Opinion Paragraph

Teacher Directions:

1. Publish Explain to children that publishing their writing is the last step in the writing process. If time permits, have children look at one another's paragraphs and incorporate any comments their classmates have. Discuss different ways technology can be used to publish writing.

2. Present Children will now have the option to present their opinion paragraphs. Have children read aloud their paragraphs to the class. Use the list below to offer children tips on listening and speaking.

While Listening to a Classmate...
- Listen carefully.
- Think of relevant questions.

While Speaking to Classmates...
- Speak clearly at an appropriate pace.
- Face the audience.

Things to Do Together...
- Build on others' ideas.
- Ask questions to check understanding.

© Common Core State Standards

Writing 1. Use a combination of drawing, dictating, and writing to compose opinion pieces in which they tell a reader the topic or the name of the book they are writing about and state an opinion or preference about the topic or book (e.g., *My favorite book is* ...)

Unit 4 Let's Go Exploring

Writing Focus: Informative/Explanatory

Name_____

Write Like a Reporter

Informative/Explanatory

Student Prompt Look at pages 12 and 13 in *Rooster's Off to See the World.* Write about why the rooster's adventure ends.

_____

_____

_____

_____

_____

_____

_____

_____

_____

Write Like a Reporter
Informative/Explanatory

> **Student Prompt, p. 114** Look at pages 12 and 13 in *Rooster's Off to See the World*. Write about why the rooster's adventure ends.

Writing to Sources Tell children to look back at the story and write about it. Help children remember that a rooster and all his animal friends decide to go off and see the world. Remind them that after the animals walk along for a while, it begins to get dark because the sun is going down. Have children listen for what happens to their adventure. Read pp. 12–13 of *Rooster's Off to See the World*. Tell children to write or dictate about why the adventure stops. Discuss with children why the animals do not want to keep going on the adventure.

Children's sentences should:

- identify and introduce a topic
- supply some details about the topic
- demonstrate strong command of the conventions of standard written English

---

Ⓒ **Common Core State Standards**

Writing 2. Use a combination of drawing, dictating, and writing to compose informative/explanatory texts in which they name what they are writing about and supply some information about the topic.

Connect the Texts

Informative/Explanatory

Name_____

Student Prompt Tell what happens at the end of *Rooster's Off to See the World.* Tell what happens at the end of "The Evening Is Coming." How are both endings alike? Write about how both stories end.

_____

_____

_____

_____

_____

_____

_____

_____

_____

_____

_____

_____

_____

_____

Connect the Texts
Informative/Explanatory

Student Prompt, p. 116 Tell what happens at the end of *Rooster's Off to See the World.* Tell what happens at the end of "The Evening Is Coming." How are both endings alike? Write about how both stories end.

Writing to Sources Tell children to look at *Rooster's Off to See the World* and "The Evening Is Coming." Read pp. 22–23 of *Rooster's Off to See the World.* Ask children how the story ends. Read "The Evening Is Coming" on page 95 of the Teacher's Edition. Ask children how it ends. Then have children discuss the endings of both stories to identify the similarities. Tell children to write or dictate their conclusion about the endings. Have them write that both stories end with nighttime coming and the animals going to bed. Children can use the following sentence frame: *At the end of the stories, nighttime came, and the animals _____.*

Score	Focus	Organization	Development of Evidence	Language and Vocabulary	Conventions
Informative/Explanatory Writing Rubric					
4	Main idea is clearly conveyed and well supported; response is focused.	Organization is clear and effective, creating a sense of cohesion.	Evidence is relevant and thorough; includes facts and details.	Ideas are clearly and effectively conveyed, using precise language and/or domain-specific vocabulary.	Command of conventions is strongly demonstrated.
3	Main idea is clear, adequately supported; response is generally focused.	Organization is clear, though minor flaws may be present and some ideas may be disconnected.	Evidence is adequate and includes facts and details.	Ideas are adequately conveyed, using both precise and more general language; may include domain-specific vocabulary.	Command of conventions is sufficiently demonstrated.
2	Main idea is somewhat supported; lacks focus or includes unnecessary material.	Organization is inconsistent, and flaws are apparent.	Evidence is uneven or incomplete; insufficient use of facts and details.	Ideas are unevenly conveyed, using overly-simplistic language; lacks domain-specific vocabulary.	Command of conventions is uneven.
1	Response may be confusing, unfocused; main idea insufficiently supported.	Organization is poor or nonexistent.	Evidence is poor or nonexistent.	Ideas are conveyed in a vague, unclear, or confusing manner.	There is very little command of conventions.
0	The response shows no evidence of the ability to construct a coherent explanatory essay using information from sources.				

© Common Core State Standards

Writing 2. Use a combination of drawing, dictating, and writing to compose informative/explanatory texts in which they name what they are writing about and supply some information about the topic.

Write Like a Reporter

Informative/Explanatory

Student Prompt Look back at pages 26 and 27 in *My Lucky Day.* Remember that Mr. Fox does many things for the piglet. Tell about what Mr. Fox does for the piglet. Write about why Mr. Fox passed out.

Write Like a Reporter

Informative/Explanatory

> **Student Prompt, p. 118** Look back at pages 26 and 27 in *My Lucky Day*. Remember that Mr. Fox does many things for the piglet. Tell about what Mr. Fox does for the piglet. Write about why Mr. Fox passed out.

Writing to Sources Tell children they are going to look back at the story and write or dictate their thoughts about it. Help them remember that Mr. Fox does many things for the piglet. Tell children to listen for what he does. Read pp. 12–21 of *My Lucky Day*. Make a list of the things that Mr. Fox does for the piglet. Record children's ideas. Encourage children to use these ideas to draw conclusions and write about why Mr. Fox passed out at the end of the day.

Children's sentences should:

- give some details about the subject
- draw a conclusion based on evidence in the story
- demonstrate strong command of the conventions of standard written English

Ⓒ **Common Core State Standards**

Writing 2. Use a combination of drawing, dictating, and writing to compose informative/explanatory texts in which they name what they are writing about and supply some information about the topic.

Connect the Texts

Informative/Explanatory

Student Prompt What lesson is in *My Lucky Day* and "The Crow and the Pitcher"? The piglet makes Mr. Fox do things for him a little at a time so that Mr. Fox won't cook him. The crow puts pebbles in the pitcher a little at a time so she can reach the water. What conclusion can you draw about the piglet and the crow? Write about them.

_____

- -

_____

- -

_____

- -

_____

- -

_____

- -

_____

- -

_____

Connect the Texts

Informative/Explanatory

Student Prompt, p. 120 What lesson is in *My Lucky Day* and "The Crow and the Pitcher"? The piglet makes Mr. Fox do things for him a little at a time so that Mr. Fox won't cook him. The crow puts pebbles in the pitcher a little at a time so she can reach the water. What conclusion can you draw about the piglet and the crow? Write about them.

Writing to Sources Review the selections *My Lucky Day* and "The Crow and the Pitcher" on page 197 of the Teacher's Edition. Have children identify the lesson of the stories: doing something a little at a time can be a good way to reach a goal. Discuss that the piglet made Mr. Fox do things a little at a time so that Mr. Fox wouldn't cook him for dinner and that the crow put pebbles in the pitcher a little at a time so that she could drink the water. Have children write or dictate their conclusions about the piglet and the crow. Children can begin by completing this sentence: *Both the piglet and the crow are* _____.

	Informative/Explanatory Writing Rubric				
Score	**Focus**	**Organization**	**Development of Evidence**	**Language and Vocabulary**	**Conventions**
4	Main idea is clearly conveyed and well supported; response is focused.	Organization is clear and effective, creating a sense of cohesion.	Evidence is relevant and thorough; includes facts and details.	Ideas are clearly and effectively conveyed, using precise language and/or domain-specific vocabulary.	Command of conventions is strongly demonstrated.
3	Main idea is clear, adequately supported; response is generally focused.	Organization is clear, though minor flaws may be present and some ideas may be disconnected.	Evidence is adequate and includes facts and details.	Ideas are adequately conveyed, using both precise and more general language; may include domain-specific vocabulary.	Command of conventions is sufficiently demonstrated.
2	Main idea is somewhat supported; lacks focus or includes unnecessary material.	Organization is inconsistent, and flaws are apparent.	Evidence is uneven or incomplete; insufficient use of facts and details.	Ideas are unevenly conveyed, using overly-simplistic language; lacks domain-specific vocabulary.	Command of conventions is uneven.
1	Response may be confusing, unfocused; main idea insufficiently supported.	Organization is poor or nonexistent.	Evidence is poor or nonexistent.	Ideas are conveyed in a vague, unclear, or confusing manner.	There is very little command of conventions.
0	The response shows no evidence of the ability to construct a coherent explanatory essay using information from sources.				

© Common Core State Standards

Writing 2. Use a combination of drawing, dictating, and writing to compose informative/explanatory texts in which they name what they are writing about and supply some information about the topic.

Write Like a Reporter

Informative/Explanatory

> **Student Prompt** Look at pages 20 and 21 in *One Little Mouse.* Listen to why Mouse doesn't want to live in the tree with the chickadees. Write about why it would be hard to live in a tree.

_____

_____

_____

_____

_____

_____

_____

_____

_____

_____

_____

_____

_____

Write Like a Reporter

Informative/Explanatory

> **Student Prompt, p. 122** Look at pages 20 and 21 in *One Little Mouse.* Listen to why Mouse doesn't want to live in the tree with the chickadees. Write about why it would be hard to live in a tree.

Writing to Sources Tell children they are going to look back at the story and write about it. Help them remember that Mouse does not want to live in the tree with the chickadees. Tell children to listen for why Mouse doesn't want to live in the tree. Read page 21 of *One Little Mouse.* Discuss with children that Mouse doesn't want to live in the tree with the chickadees because a branch would not be a good pillow. Now have the children use the words and pictures from *One Little Mouse* to help them write or dictate their ideas about why it would be hard to live in a tree.

Children's sentences should:

- identify the topic
- supply some ideas about the topic
- demonstrate strong command of the conventions of standard written English

---

Ⓒ Common Core State Standards

Writing 2. Use a combination of drawing, dictating, and writing to compose informative/explanatory texts in which they name what they are writing about and supply some information about the topic.

Connect the Texts
Informative/Explanatory

Student Prompt Think about how the animals made their houses in *One Little Mouse.* Look at the materials used in "Make a Kazoo!" Are any of the materials the same? Write to explain why the materials in "Make a Kazoo!" wouldn't make a very good house.

_____

- -

_____

- -

_____

- -

_____

- -

_____

- -

_____

- -

_____

Connect the Texts
Informative/Explanatory

Student Prompt, p. 124 Think about how the animals made their houses in *One Little Mouse.* Look at the materials used in "Make a Kazoo!" Are any of the materials the same? Write to explain why the materials in "Make a Kazoo!" wouldn't make a very good house.

Writing to Sources Have children discuss and make a list of how the different animals made their houses in *One Little Mouse.* Then have children look at the materials in "Make a Kazoo!" on pp. 296–297 in *My Skills Buddy* (page 297 in the Teacher's Edition). Ask children if any of the materials are the same. Have children write or dictate why the kazoo materials wouldn't make a very good house.

Informative/Explanatory Writing Rubric					
Score	Focus	Organization	Development of Evidence	Language and Vocabulary	Conventions
4	Main idea is clearly conveyed and well supported; response is focused.	Organization is clear and effective, creating a sense of cohesion.	Evidence is relevant and thorough; includes facts and details.	Ideas are clearly and effectively conveyed, using precise language and/or domain-specific vocabulary.	Command of conventions is strongly demonstrated.
3	Main idea is clear, adequately supported; response is generally focused.	Organization is clear, though minor flaws may be present and some ideas may be disconnected.	Evidence is adequate and includes facts and details.	Ideas are adequately conveyed, using both precise and more general language; may include domain-specific vocabulary.	Command of conventions is sufficiently demonstrated.
2	Main idea is somewhat supported; lacks focus or includes unnecessary material.	Organization is inconsistent, and flaws are apparent.	Evidence is uneven or incomplete; insufficient use of facts and details.	Ideas are unevenly conveyed, using overly-simplistic language; lacks domain-specific vocabulary.	Command of conventions is uneven.
1	Response may be confusing, unfocused; main idea insufficiently supported.	Organization is poor or nonexistent.	Evidence is poor or nonexistent.	Ideas are conveyed in a vague, unclear, or confusing manner.	There is very little command of conventions.
0	The response shows no evidence of the ability to construct a coherent explanatory essay using information from sources.				

© **Common Core State Standards**

Writing 2. Use a combination of drawing, dictating, and writing to compose informative/explanatory texts in which they name what they are writing about and supply some information about the topic.

Name_____

Write Like a Reporter

Informative/Explanatory

> **Student Prompt** Look at pages 2 and 3 of *Goldilocks and the Three Bears.* Write sentences to describe the father bear, mother bear, and baby bear. Use details from the words and the pictures.

_____

- -

_____

- -

_____

- -

_____

- -

_____

- -

_____

- -

_____

- -

_____

- -

_____

Write Like a Reporter
Informative/Explanatory

> **Student Prompt, p. 126** Look at pages 2 and 3 of *Goldilocks and the Three Bears.* Write sentences to describe the father bear, mother bear, and baby bear. Use details from the words and the pictures.

Writing to Sources Have children look back at the text and write or dictate their thoughts about it. Help them remember that Goldilocks goes into the bears' home and uses their things. Read pages 3 and 21 of *Goldilocks and the Three Bears* and tell children to listen for details that describe the bears. Discuss with children the details that describe the bears such as their size and their voices. Children can use these details to describe the bears in their writing.

Children's sentences should:

- identify and focus on the details of the topic
- supply some facts about the details of the topic
- draw a conclusion from the text
- demonstrate strong command of the conventions of standard written English

Ⓒ **Common Core State Standards**

Writing 2. Use a combination of drawing, dictating, and writing to compose informative/explanatory texts in which they name what they are writing about and supply some information about the topic.

Name_____

Connect the Texts
Informative/Explanatory

> **Student Prompt** Think about the main characters from *Goldilocks and the Three Bears* and "How the Fly Saved the River." Find ways Goldilocks and the moose are alike in the texts. Write about how they are alike.

Connect the Texts
Informative/Explanatory

Student Prompt, p. 128 Think about the main characters from *Goldilocks and the Three Bears* and "How the Fly Saved the River." Find ways Goldilocks and the moose are alike in the texts. Write about how they are alike.

Writing to Sources Have children go back and review the selections *Goldilocks and the Three Bears* and "How the Fly Saved the River" on pp. 90–91 in *My Skills Buddy* (Teacher's Edition, p. 399). Tell them to think about the characters Goldilocks and the moose. Help children use the text to draw conclusions about how Goldilocks and the moose are alike. List their responses on the board. Children can use ideas from the list to complete the following sentence frame: *Goldilocks and the moose both _____*.

		Informative/Explanatory Writing Rubric			
Score	**Focus**	**Organization**	**Development of Evidence**	**Language and Vocabulary**	**Conventions**
4	Main idea is clearly conveyed and well supported; response is focused.	Organization is clear and effective, creating a sense of cohesion.	Evidence is relevant and thorough; includes facts and details.	Ideas are clearly and effectively conveyed, using precise language and/or domain-specific vocabulary.	Command of conventions is strongly demonstrated.
3	Main idea is clear, adequately supported; response is generally focused.	Organization is clear, though minor flaws may be present and some ideas may be disconnected.	Evidence is adequate and includes facts and details.	Ideas are adequately conveyed, using both precise and more general language; may include domain-specific vocabulary.	Command of conventions is sufficiently demonstrated.
2	Main idea is somewhat supported; lacks focus or includes unnecessary material.	Organization is inconsistent, and flaws are apparent.	Evidence is uneven or incomplete; insufficient use of facts and details.	Ideas are unevenly conveyed, using overly-simplistic language; lacks domain-specific vocabulary.	Command of conventions is uneven.
1	Response may be confusing, unfocused; main idea insufficiently supported.	Organization is poor or nonexistent.	Evidence is poor or nonexistent.	Ideas are conveyed in a vague, unclear, or confusing manner.	There is very little command of conventions.
0	The response shows no evidence of the ability to construct a coherent explanatory essay using information from sources.				

© **Common Core State Standards**

Writing 2. Use a combination of drawing, dictating, and writing to compose informative/explanatory texts in which they name what they are writing about and supply some information about the topic.

Name_____

Write Like a Reporter
Informative/Explanatory

Student Prompt Look at pages 10–13 of *If You Could Go to Antarctica.* Describe the penguins in the pictures. Draw a picture of a penguin. Write why penguins are different from other birds.

_____

- -

_____

_____

- -

_____

_____

- -

_____

_____

- -

_____

_____

- -

_____

Write Like a Reporter
Informative/Explanatory

Student Prompt, p. 130 Look at pages 10–13 of *If You Could Go to Antarctica*. Describe the penguins in the pictures. Draw a picture of a penguin. Write why penguins are different from other birds.

Writing to Sources Tell children that they will look back and review the selection *If You Could Go to Antarctica.* Have them look at the pictures of the penguins on pages 10–13. Ask children how they are different from other birds. Then have them discuss how penguins are different from other birds with a partner. Invite children to draw pictures of penguins and to use these pictures as inspiration to write or dictate stories about why penguins are different from other birds.

Children's sentences should:

- compare penguins with other birds
- give some facts about penguins and other birds
- demonstrate strong command of the conventions of standard written English

Ⓒ **Common Core State Standards**

Writing 2. Use a combination of drawing, dictating, and writing to compose informative/explanatory texts in which they name what they are writing about and supply some information about the topic.

Name _____

Connect the Texts

Informative/Explanatory

Student Prompt Look at the pictures on pages 20 and 21 of *If You Could Go to Antarctica.* Look at the pictures in "One, Two, Buckle My Shoe." Describe what the people in the pictures are wearing. Write about what kind of weather people usually wear this type of clothing in.

_____

- -

_____

- -

_____

- -

_____

- -

_____

- -

_____

- -

_____

Connect the Texts
Informative/Explanatory

Student Prompt, p. 132 Look at the pictures on pages 20 and 21 of *If You Could Go to Antarctica*. Look at the pictures in "One, Two, Buckle My Shoe." Describe what the people in the pictures are wearing. Write about what kind of weather people usually wear this type of clothing in.

Writing to Sources Review the photographs in *If You Could Go to Antarctica* and the illustrations in "One, Two, Buckle My Shoe" on pp. 110–111 in *My Skills Buddy*. Tell children to pay attention to the clothing people are wearing. Ask them to describe what the people are wearing. Tell children to use the pictures to draw conclusions and write or dictate about what kind of weather people usually wear this type of clothing in.

	Informative/Explanatory Writing Rubric				
Score	**Focus**	**Organization**	**Development of Evidence**	**Language and Vocabulary**	**Conventions**
4	Main idea is clearly conveyed and well supported; response is focused.	Organization is clear and effective, creating a sense of cohesion.	Evidence is relevant and thorough; includes facts and details.	Ideas are clearly and effectively conveyed, using precise language and/or domain-specific vocabulary.	Command of conventions is strongly demonstrated.
3	Main idea is clear, adequately supported; response is generally focused.	Organization is clear, though minor flaws may be present and some ideas may be disconnected.	Evidence is adequate and includes facts and details.	Ideas are adequately conveyed, using both precise and more general language; may include domain-specific vocabulary.	Command of conventions is sufficiently demonstrated.
2	Main idea is somewhat supported; lacks focus or includes unnecessary material.	Organization is inconsistent, and flaws are apparent.	Evidence is uneven or incomplete; insufficient use of facts and details.	Ideas are unevenly conveyed, using overly-simplistic language; lacks domain-specific vocabulary.	Command of conventions is uneven.
1	Response may be confusing, unfocused; main idea insufficiently supported.	Organization is poor or nonexistent.	Evidence is poor or nonexistent.	Ideas are conveyed in a vague, unclear, or confusing manner.	There is very little command of conventions.
0	The response shows no evidence of the ability to construct a coherent explanatory essay using information from sources.				

ⓒ Common Core State Standards

Writing 2. Use a combination of drawing, dictating, and writing to compose informative/explanatory texts in which they name what they are writing about and supply some information about the topic.

Write Like a Reporter

Informative/Explanatory

> **Student Prompt** Look at pages 28 and 29 of *Abuela*.
> Tell about the clouds that Rosalba and Abuela see.
> Write sentences that summarize the places Rosalba
> and Abuela go and the kinds of clouds they see.

_____

- -

_____

- -

_____

- -

_____

- -

_____

- -

_____

- -

_____

- -

_____

Write Like a Reporter
Informative/Explanatory

Student Prompt, p. 134 Look at pages 28 and 29 of *Abuela*. Tell about the clouds that Rosalba and Abuela see. Write sentences that summarize the places Rosalba and Abuela go and the kinds of clouds they see.

Writing to Sources Tell children that they are going to look back at the story and write about it. Help them remember that Rosalba and Abuela sit in the clouds. Have children listen for what the clouds look like to the characters. Read page 28 of *Abuela*. Tell children to visualize all of the places Rosalba and Abuela go and to visualize the clouds that Rosalba and Abuela see. Encourage children to use these visualizations to write or dictate their sentences.

Children's sentences should:

- visualize the topic
- tell about the details of the topic
- demonstrate strong command of the conventions of standard written English

© **Common Core State Standards**

Writing 2. Use a combination of drawing, dictating, and writing to compose informative/explanatory texts in which they name what they are writing about and supply some information about the topic.

Connect the Texts

Informative/Explanatory

Student Prompt Look at the pictures in "The Statue of Liberty." Picture the Statue of Liberty on a cloudy day. Write what the clouds might look like. How do the clouds look like the clouds in the selection *Abuela?*

_____

_____

_____

_____

_____

_____

_____

_____

_____

_____

_____

Connect the Texts
Informative/Explanatory

Student Prompt, p. 136 Look at the pictures in "The Statue of Liberty." Picture the Statue of Liberty on a cloudy day. Write what the clouds might look like. How do the clouds look like the clouds in the selection *Abuela*?

Writing to Sources Tell children to study the pictures in "The Statue of Liberty" on pp. 130–131 in *My Skills Buddy.* Have them discuss what the statue would look like with clouds in front of it. Ask them to write or dictate sentences that describe how the clouds might look, and if they look like the clouds in the selection *Abuela*.

Informative/Explanatory Writing Rubric					
Score	**Focus**	**Organization**	**Development of Evidence**	**Language and Vocabulary**	**Conventions**
4	Main idea is clearly conveyed and well supported; response is focused.	Organization is clear and effective, creating a sense of cohesion.	Evidence is relevant and thorough; includes facts and details.	Ideas are clearly and effectively conveyed, using precise language and/or domain-specific vocabulary.	Command of conventions is strongly demonstrated.
3	Main idea is clear, adequately supported; response is generally focused.	Organization is clear, though minor flaws may be present and some ideas may be disconnected.	Evidence is adequate and includes facts and details.	Ideas are adequately conveyed, using both precise and more general language; may include domain-specific vocabulary.	Command of conventions is sufficiently demonstrated.
2	Main idea is somewhat supported; lacks focus or includes unnecessary material.	Organization is inconsistent, and flaws are apparent.	Evidence is uneven or incomplete; insufficient use of facts and details.	Ideas are unevenly conveyed, using overly-simplistic language; lacks domain-specific vocabulary.	Command of conventions is uneven.
1	Response may be confusing, unfocused; main idea insufficiently supported.	Organization is poor or nonexistent.	Evidence is poor or nonexistent.	Ideas are conveyed in a vague, unclear, or confusing manner.	There is very little command of conventions.
0	The response shows no evidence of the ability to construct a coherent explanatory essay using information from sources.				

© **Common Core State Standards**

Writing 2. Use a combination of drawing, dictating, and writing to compose informative/explanatory texts in which they name what they are writing about and supply some information about the topic.

Prove It!
Short Report

Antarctica

Short Report

In this unit, children have read examples of informative/explanatory writing and have had the opportunity to write in this mode. Remind children of texts and writing tasks (such as Write Like a Reporter) in which they have encountered and practiced informative/explanatory writing.

Key Features of a Short Report

- is a short informational article
- has a clear topic sentence
- gives facts and details about a real-life topic
- presents information in an organized way

Writing Task Overview

Each unit writing task provides children with an opportunity to write using information from a selection they are reading. To successfully complete the task, children must understand and interpret the selection and create their own response.

Antarctica

Part 1: Children will reread a selection identified from this unit. They will then respond to this selection and discuss their written response with partners.

Part 2: Children will work individually to plan, write, and revise their own short report.

Scorable Products: evidence-based short response, short report

Antarctica: Writing Task – Short Response

Teacher Directions:

1. Introduce the Source Reread the following Big Book selection:

If You Could Go to Antarctica

Explain to children that they will use the words and illustrations in the book to respond. Tell children that they will also write their own short reports that use information from the text.

2. Have children draw a picture of something they can find in Antarctica based on the information in *If You Could Go to Antarctica.*

3. Using evidence from the text, have children write or dictate a sentence that gives a detail or fact about what they have chosen to draw.

© **Common Core State Standards**

Writing 2. Use a combination of drawing, dictating, and writing to compose informative/explanatory texts in which they name what they are writing about and supply some information about the topic.

Scoring Information

Use the following 2-point scoring rubric to evaluate children's answers to the evidence-based short response.

Analysis Rubric	
2	The response: • demonstrates the ability to analyze facts and details in order to give information about something you can see in Antarctica • includes specific details that make reference to the text
1	The response: • demonstrates a limited ability to analyze facts and details in order to give information about something you can see in Antarctica • includes some details that make reference to the text
0	A response receives no credit if it demonstrates no ability to analyze information or includes no relevant details from the text.

Ⓒ Common Core State Standards

Writing 2. Use a combination of drawing, dictating, and writing to compose informative/explanatory texts in which they name what they are writing about and supply some information about the topic.

Name _____

Antarctica

Writing Task – Short Response

Draw a picture of something you can see in Antarctica.

Name _____

Write a sentence that tells about your picture.

_____

- -

_____

- -

_____

- -

_____

- -

_____

- -

_____

- -

_____

- -

_____

- -

_____

Antarctica: Writing Task – Short Report

Teacher Directions:

1. Have children draw a picture of three things they can find in Antarctica based on the information in *If You Could Go to Antarctica*.

2. Have children write or dictate a short report that gives facts or details from the selection about what they have chosen to draw.

3. Scoring Information Use the scoring rubric on the next page to evaluate children's short reports.

© **Common Core State Standards**

Writing 2. Use a combination of drawing, dictating, and writing to compose informative/explanatory texts in which they name what they are writing about and supply some information about the topic.

Informative/Explanatory Writing Rubric					
Score	Focus	Organization	Development of Evidence	Language and Vocabulary	Conventions
4	Main idea is clearly stated.	Organization is clear.	Evidence includes many facts and details.	Ideas are clearly and effectively conveyed, using precise words.	Command of conventions is strongly demonstrated.
3	Main idea is adequately stated.	Organization is clear, though minor flaws may be present.	Evidence includes some facts and details.	Ideas are adequately conveyed, using precise words.	Command of conventions is sufficiently demonstrated.
2	Main idea is somewhat stated.	Organization is inconsistent.	Evidence has insufficient use of facts or details.	Ideas are unevenly conveyed, using overly simplistic language.	Command of conventions is uneven.
1	Response may be unfocused.	Organization is poor or nonexistent.	Evidence is poor or nonexistent.	Ideas are conveyed in a vague or confusing manner.	There is very little command of conventions.
0	The response shows no evidence of the ability to construct a coherent expository paragraph using information from sources.				

Ⓒ Common Core State Standards

Writing 2. Use a combination of drawing, dictating, and writing to compose informative/explanatory texts in which they name what they are writing about and supply some information about the topic.

Antarctica

Writing Task – Short Report

Short Report Prompt

Draw a picture of three things you can see in Antarctica. Write a paragraph that tells about your picture. Your report should tell facts about the three things.

Name _____

Antarctica: Writing Task – Short Report

Teacher Directions:

1. Publish Explain to children that publishing their writing is the last step in the writing process. If time permits, have children review one another's reports and incorporate any comments their classmates have. Discuss different ways technology can be used to publish writing.

2. Present Children will now have the option to present their short reports. Have children give speeches on their reports in front of the class. Use the list below to offer children some tips on listening and speaking.

While Listening to a Classmate...
- Think about what the speaker is saying.
- Raise your hand to ask a question.

While Speaking to Classmates...
- Stay on topic.
- Speak clearly.

Things to Do Together...
- Follow agreed-upon discussion rules.
- Ask and answer questions.

Ⓒ **Common Core State Standards**

Writing 2. Use a combination of drawing, dictating, and writing to compose informative/explanatory texts in which they name what they are writing about and supply some information about the topic.

Unit 5 Going Places

Writing Focus: Argument

Write Like a Reporter
Argument

Student Prompt In *Max Takes the Train,* look at the ways Max and Uncle Bunny got to Zeke's Palace of Ice Cream. Look at the way Ruby got to Zeke's Palace of Ice Cream. Write who got there faster. Why did they arrive faster?

_____

- -

_____

- -

_____

- -

_____

- -

_____

- -

_____

- -

_____

Write Like a Reporter

Argument

> **Student Prompt, p. 150** In *Max Takes the Train,* look at the ways Max and Uncle Bunny got to Zeke's Palace of Ice Cream. Look at the way Ruby got to Zeke's Palace of Ice Cream. Write who got there faster. Why did they arrive faster?

Writing to Sources Direct children to look back at the story *Max Takes the Train* and write about it. Help them recall that Max and Uncle Bunny traveled on a bus, a train, a ferryboat, a plane, and the subway. Help them remember that Ruby traveled on a bike. Now have them write their ideas. Ask children which character or characters got to Zeke's Palace of Ice Cream faster. Tell children to write their responses. They can use the sentence frame: *I think that _____ got to Zeke's Palace of Ice Cream faster because _____.* Discuss arguments for both sides. Make sure children use facts and details from the story to support their claims.

Children's sentences should:

- introduce the topic
- state an opinion
- supply a reason for the opinion
- demonstrate strong command of the conventions of standard written English

---

Ⓒ **Common Core State Standards**

Writing 1. Use a combination of drawing, dictating, and writing to compose opinion pieces in which they tell a reader the topic or the name of the book they are writing about and state an opinion or preference about the topic or book (e.g., *My favorite book is...*).

Name_____

Connect the Texts

Argument

> **Student Prompt** Think about all of the ways Max and Uncle Bunny traveled. Listen to "The Swing" and look at the picture of the girl on p. 30. Which way do you think she would like to travel? Write about it and tell why you think so.

_____

- - - - - - - - - - - - - - - - - - -

_____

- - - - - - - - - - - - - - - - - - -

_____

- - - - - - - - - - - - - - - - - - -

_____

- - - - - - - - - - - - - - - - - - -

_____

- - - - - - - - - - - - - - - - - - -

_____

Connect the Texts
Argument

> **Student Prompt, p. 152** Think about all of the ways Max and Uncle Bunny traveled. Listen to "The Swing" and look at the picture of the girl on p. 30. Which way do you think she would like to travel? Write about it and tell why you think so.

Writing to Sources Tell children to look at the pictures of all of the ways Max and Uncle Bunny traveled in *Max Takes the Train*. Have children listen to "The Swing" (Teacher's Edition, page 97) and look at the girl swinging on page 30 in *My Skills Buddy*. Ask children to think about which kind of travel they think the girl would enjoy and why. Children can complete this sentence frame using evidence from the story and poem: *I think that the girl would like to _____ because _____.* Children can draw a picture of the girl traveling.

4-point Argument Writing Rubric					
Score	**Statement of Purpose/Focus**	**Organization**	**Development of Evidence**	**Language and Vocabulary**	**Conventions**
4	Opinion is clearly conveyed and well supported; response is focused.	Organization is clear and effective, creating a sense of cohesion.	Evidence is thorough and persuasive, and includes facts and details.	Ideas are clearly and effectively conveyed, using precise language and/or domain-specific vocabulary.	Command of conventions is strongly demonstrated.
3	Opinion is clear, adequately supported; response is generally focused.	Organization is clear, though minor flaws may be present and some ideas may be disconnected.	Evidence is adequate and includes facts and details.	Ideas are adequately conveyed, using both precise and more general language; may include domain-specific vocabulary.	Command of conventions is sufficiently demonstrated.
2	Opinion is somewhat supported; response may lack focus or include unnecessary material.	Organization is inconsistent, and flaws are apparent.	Evidence is uneven or incomplete; insufficient use of facts and details.	Ideas are unevenly conveyed, using overly-simplistic language; lack of domain-specific vocabulary.	Command of conventions is uneven.
1	The response may be confusing, unfocused; opinion not sufficiently supported.	Organization is poor or nonexistent.	Evidence is poor or nonexistent.	Ideas are conveyed in a vague, unclear, or confusing manner.	There is very little command of conventions.
0	The response shows no evidence of the ability to construct a coherent opinion essay using information from sources.				

Ⓒ Common Core State Standards

Writing 1. Use a combination of drawing, dictating, and writing to compose opinion pieces in which they tell a reader the topic or the name of the book they are writing about and state an opinion or preference about the topic or book (e.g., *My favorite book is...*).

Name_____

Write Like a Reporter
Argument

Student Prompt Think about how the Coast Guard rescued the sailors in *Mayday! Mayday!* Would you want to be a Coast Guard rescuer when you grow up? Explain your reasons.

_____

_____

_____

_____

_____

_____

_____

_____

_____

_____

_____

Write Like a Reporter
Argument

Student Prompt, p. 154 Think about how the Coast Guard rescued the sailors in *Mayday! Mayday!* Would you want to be a Coast Guard rescuer when you grow up? Explain your reasons.

Writing to Sources Tell children to look back at the story *Mayday! Mayday!* and write about it. Help children remember that the Coast Guard does many things in order to rescue the people on the yacht. Read pp. 18–19. Now help children make a list of the things that the Coast Guard does to rescue the sailors. Children can use the list to focus on the parts of the job and write about whether they want to be in the Coast Guard or not. Children can use this sentence frame to begin their argument: *I _____ to be in the Coast Guard when I grow up because _____.* Remind them to use facts and details from the text to support their opinion.

Children's sentences should:

- introduce a claim
- state a claim or opinion
- demonstrate strong command of the conventions of standard written English

Ⓒ Common Core State Standards

Writing 1. Use a combination of drawing, dictating, and writing to compose opinion pieces in which they tell a reader the topic or the name of the book they are writing about and state an opinion or preference about the topic or book (e.g., *My favorite book is...*).

Name_____

Connect the Texts
Argument

> **Student Prompt** Look at the pictures of the wind in *Mayday! Mayday!* Look at the pictures of the wind in "The Wind and the Sun." Is the wind strong or weak in *Mayday! Mayday!?* Write how you know. Is the wind strong or weak in "The Wind and the Sun"? Write how you know.

_____

_____

_____

_____

_____

_____

_____

_____

_____

_____

Connect the Texts
Argument

Student Prompt, p. 156 Look at the pictures of the wind in *Mayday! Mayday!*
Look at the pictures of the wind in "The Wind and the Sun." Is the wind strong
or weak in *Mayday! Mayday!?* Write how you know. Is the wind strong or weak in
"The Wind and the Sun"? Write how you know.

Writing to Sources Review *Mayday! Mayday!* and "The Wind and the Sun"
(Teacher's Edition, page 203). Read page 18 of *Mayday! Mayday!* Ask children if the
wind is strong or weak. Ask children how they know. Encourage children to use the
text and the pictures in "The Wind and the Sun." Ask children if the wind is strong or
weak. Ask children how they know. Remind children to use specific evidence from
the words and pictures for support. Children can use these sentence frames:

The wind in Mayday! Mayday! *is _____. I know it is _____ because _____.*

The wind in "The Wind and the Sun" is _____. I know it is _____ because _____.

\multicolumn{6}{c}{**4-point Argument Writing Rubric**}
Score	**Statement of Purpose/Focus**	**Organization**	**Development of Evidence**	**Language and Vocabulary**	**Conventions**
4	Opinion is clearly conveyed and well supported; response is focused.	Organization is clear and effective, creating a sense of cohesion.	Evidence is thorough and persuasive, and includes facts and details.	Ideas are clearly and effectively conveyed, using precise language and/or domain-specific vocabulary.	Command of conventions is strongly demonstrated.
3	Opinion is clear, adequately supported; response is generally focused.	Organization is clear, though minor flaws may be present and some ideas may be disconnected.	Evidence is adequate and includes facts and details.	Ideas are adequately conveyed, using both precise and more general language; may include domain-specific vocabulary.	Command of conventions is sufficiently demonstrated.
2	Opinion is somewhat supported; response may lack focus or include unnecessary material.	Organization is inconsistent, and flaws are apparent.	Evidence is uneven or incomplete; insufficient use of facts and details.	Ideas are unevenly conveyed, using overly-simplistic language; lack of domain-specific vocabulary.	Command of conventions is uneven.
1	The response may be confusing, unfocused; opinion not sufficiently supported.	Organization is poor or nonexistent.	Evidence is poor or nonexistent.	Ideas are conveyed in a vague, unclear, or confusing manner.	There is very little command of conventions.
0	\multicolumn{5}{l}{The response shows no evidence of the ability to construct a coherent opinion essay using information from sources.}

 **Common Core State Standards**

Writing 1. Use a combination of drawing, dictating, and writing to compose opinion pieces in which they tell a reader the topic or the name of the
book they are writing about and state an opinion or preference about the topic or book (e.g., *My favorite book is...*).

Name_____

Write Like a Reporter
Argument

> **Student Prompt** Look at pages 14 and 15 in *Trucks Roll!* The dispatcher tells the truck drivers where to take the things they are carrying. Would you rather be a dispatcher or a truck driver? Why?

_____

_____

_____

_____

_____

_____

_____

_____

_____

_____

_____

Write Like a Reporter
Argument

> **Student Prompt, p. 158** Look at pages 14 and 15 in *Trucks Roll!* The dispatcher tells the truck drivers where to take the things they are carrying. Would you rather be a dispatcher or a truck driver? Why?

Writing to Sources Have children look back at the story *Trucks Roll!* and tell them that they will be writing about it. Help children recall that truck drivers take many different things where they need to go. Tell children that dispatchers tell the truck drivers where they need to take the things. Read pp. 14–15. Write a list of what the dispatcher does and what the truck driver does. Using evidence from the text, have children write which job they would rather do. Children can use the sentence frame: *I would rather be a _____ because _____.*

Children's sentences should:

- introduce the topics
- choose a preference from the two topics
- demonstrate strong command of the conventions of standard written English

---

Ⓒ **Common Core State Standards**

Writing 1. Use a combination of drawing, dictating, and writing to compose opinion pieces in which they tell a reader the topic or the name of the book they are writing about and state an opinion or preference about the topic or book (e.g., *My favorite book is...*).

Connect the Texts

Argument

> **Student Prompt** In "Going Downtown," Lucy looked
> for signs and followed their directions to find a parking
> space. Do you think truck drivers need to pay attention
> to signs too? What could have happened if Lucy or the
> truck drivers didn't pay attention to signs?

_____

- -

_____

- -

_____

- -

_____

- -

_____

- -

_____

- -

_____

Connect the Texts
Argument

Student Prompt, p. 160 In "Going Downtown," Lucy looked for signs and followed their directions to find a parking space. Do you think truck drivers need to pay attention to signs too? What could have happened if Lucy or the truck drivers didn't pay attention to signs?

Writing to Sources Have children look at the signs in "Going Downtown" in *My Skills Buddy,* pp. 70–71. Make a list of the signs Lucy sees and follows. Ask children if they can think of any other road signs and include them in the list. Ask children to write if they think the truck drivers from *Trucks Roll!* need to look for and follow road signs. Ask children to write what could have happened if Lucy or the truck drivers didn't pay attention to signs. Tell children to use the list of road signs and evidence from the text to help them draw conclusions for their written answers.

	4-point Argument Writing Rubric				
Score	**Statement of Purpose/Focus**	**Organization**	**Development of Evidence**	**Language and Vocabulary**	**Conventions**
4	Opinion is clearly conveyed and well supported; response is focused.	Organization is clear and effective, creating a sense of cohesion.	Evidence is thorough and persuasive, and includes facts and details.	Ideas are clearly and effectively conveyed, using precise language and/or domain-specific vocabulary.	Command of conventions is strongly demonstrated.
3	Opinion is clear, adequately supported; response is generally focused.	Organization is clear, though minor flaws may be present and some ideas may be disconnected.	Evidence is adequate and includes facts and details.	Ideas are adequately conveyed, using both precise and more general language; may include domain-specific vocabulary.	Command of conventions is sufficiently demonstrated.
2	Opinion is somewhat supported; response may lack focus or include unnecessary material.	Organization is inconsistent, and flaws are apparent.	Evidence is uneven or incomplete; insufficient use of facts and details.	Ideas are unevenly conveyed, using overly-simplistic language; lack of domain-specific vocabulary.	Command of conventions is uneven.
1	The response may be confusing, unfocused; opinion not sufficiently supported.	Organization is poor or nonexistent.	Evidence is poor or nonexistent.	Ideas are conveyed in a vague, unclear, or confusing manner.	There is very little command of conventions.
0	The response shows no evidence of the ability to construct a coherent opinion essay using information from sources.				

Ⓒ **Common Core State Standards**

Writing 1. Use a combination of drawing, dictating, and writing to compose opinion pieces in which they tell a reader the topic or the name of the book they are writing about and state an opinion or preference about the topic or book (e.g., *My favorite book is...*).

Name_____

Write Like a Reporter

Argument

Student Prompt Look at the different kinds of engines in *The Little Engine That Could*. Talk about the things that the engines carried. Choose one of the engines. Write what you would want to carry if you were an engine. Tell why you would want to carry that.

_____

- -

_____

- -

_____

- -

_____

- -

_____

- -

_____

- -

_____

Write Like a Reporter
Argument

> **Student Prompt, p. 162** Look at the different kinds of engines in *The Little Engine That Could*. Talk about the things that the engines carried. Choose one of the engines. Write what you would want to carry if you were an engine. Tell why you would want to carry that.

Writing to Sources Have children look back at the story *The Little Engine That Could* and write about it. Help them remember that the toys on the train ask many different engines for help. The engines all carried different things. Make a list of the different things the engines carried. Ask children what they would want to carry if they were one of the engines. Discuss with children their reasons for wanting to carry those things. Children can use the sentence frame: *If I were an engine, I would want to carry _____.* Remind them to support their opinions with reasons.

Children's sentences should:

- introduce the topic from the book
- state a personal preference
- talk about a reason for the preference
- demonstrate strong command of the conventions of standard written English

Ⓒ **Common Core State Standards**

Writing 1. Use a combination of drawing, dictating, and writing to compose opinion pieces in which they tell a reader the topic or the name of the book they are writing about and state an opinion or preference about the topic or book (e.g., *My favorite book is...*).

Name_____

Connect the Texts

Argument

> **Student Prompt** Who is your favorite character—Little Blue Engine from *The Little Engine That Could* or Fox from "Queen of the Forest"? Write about your favorite character. Tell why that character is your favorite.

_____

_____

_____

_____

_____

_____

_____

_____

_____

_____

Connect the Texts
Argument

Student Prompt, p. 164 Who is your favorite character—Little Blue Engine from *The Little Engine That Could* or Fox from "Queen of the Forest"? Write about your favorite character. Tell why that character is your favorite.

Writing to Sources Have children look back and review the selections *The Little Engine That Could* and "Queen of the Forest" *(My Skills Buddy,* pp. 90–91; Teacher's Edition, pp. 406–407). Talk about the little engine character and what she does. Then ask children whether or not they like the little engine. Talk about the fox and what she does. Then ask children whether or not they like the fox. Have them begin by completing this sentence frame: *My favorite character is _____.* Remind children to support their choices with reasons.

4-point Argument Writing Rubric				
Score	Statement of Purpose/Focus	Organization	Development of Evidence	Language and Vocabulary	Conventions
4	Opinion is clearly conveyed and well supported; response is focused.	Organization is clear and effective, creating a sense of cohesion.	Evidence is thorough and persuasive, and includes facts and details.	Ideas are clearly and effectively conveyed, using precise language and/or domain-specific vocabulary.	Command of conventions is strongly demonstrated.
3	Opinion is clear, adequately supported; response is generally focused.	Organization is clear, though minor flaws may be present and some ideas may be disconnected.	Evidence is adequate and includes facts and details.	Ideas are adequately conveyed, using both precise and more general language; may include domain-specific vocabulary.	Command of conventions is sufficiently demonstrated.
2	Opinion is somewhat supported; response may lack focus or include unnecessary material.	Organization is inconsistent, and flaws are apparent.	Evidence is uneven or incomplete; insufficient use of facts and details.	Ideas are unevenly conveyed, using overly-simplistic language; lack of domain-specific vocabulary.	Command of conventions is uneven.
1	The response may be confusing, unfocused; opinion not sufficiently supported.	Organization is poor or nonexistent.	Evidence is poor or nonexistent.	Ideas are conveyed in a vague, unclear, or confusing manner.	There is very little command of conventions.
0	The response shows no evidence of the ability to construct a coherent opinion essay using information from sources.				

© **Common Core State Standards**

Writing 1. Use a combination of drawing, dictating, and writing to compose opinion pieces in which they tell a reader the topic or the name of the book they are writing about and state an opinion or preference about the topic or book (e.g., *My favorite book is...*).

Write Like a Reporter

Argument

Student Prompt Look at pictures and text in *On the Move!* Which kind of transportation pictured on these pages would you want to take? Tell why you chose that way to travel.

_____

_____

_____

_____

_____

_____

_____

_____

_____

_____

_____

_____

_____

Write Like a Reporter

Argument

> **Student Prompt, p. 166** Look at pictures and text in *On the Move!* Which kind of transportation pictured on these pages would you want to take? Tell why you chose that way to travel.

Writing to Sources Tell children to go back and review *On the Move!* Tell children to look at the pictures of all of the different ways to travel. Ask children to choose a mode of transportation described in the selection that they would want to use. Have children tell why they would choose that kind of transportation.

Children's sentences should:

- think about the topic
- give an opinion
- give an explanation
- demonstrate strong command of the conventions of standard written English

Ⓒ **Common Core State Standards**

Writing 1. Use a combination of drawing, dictating, and writing to compose opinion pieces in which they tell a reader the topic or the name of the book they are writing about and state an opinion or preference about the topic or book (e.g., *My favorite book is...*).

Connect the Texts

Argument

Student Prompt Look at the pictures of animals on pages 12, 13, and 15 in *On the Move!* Look at the horses in "All the Pretty Little Horses." Write why horses would be good at helping people get where they want to go.

_____

_____

_____

_____

_____

_____

_____

_____

_____

_____

Connect the Texts
Argument

> **Student Prompt, p. 168** Look at the pictures of animals on pages 12, 13, and 15 in *On the Move!* Look at the horses in "All the Pretty Little Horses." Write why horses would be good at helping people get where they want to go.

Writing to Sources Tell children to review the photographs in *On the Move!* and the illustration in "All the Pretty Little Horses" in *My Skills Buddy,* pp. 110–111. Tell children to think about ways people can use horses to travel. Ask children to write why they think horses would be good at helping people travel. Children can use the sentence frame: *I think horses could help people get where they want to go because* _____.

Score	Statement of Purpose/Focus	Organization	Development of Evidence	Language and Vocabulary	Conventions
	4-point Argument Writing Rubric				
4	Opinion is clearly conveyed and well supported; response is focused.	Organization is clear and effective, creating a sense of cohesion.	Evidence is thorough and persuasive, and includes facts and details.	Ideas are clearly and effectively conveyed, using precise language and/or domain-specific vocabulary.	Command of conventions is strongly demonstrated.
3	Opinion is clear, adequately supported; response is generally focused.	Organization is clear, though minor flaws may be present and some ideas may be disconnected.	Evidence is adequate and includes facts and details.	Ideas are adequately conveyed, using both precise and more general language; may include domain-specific vocabulary.	Command of conventions is sufficiently demonstrated.
2	Opinion is somewhat supported; response may lack focus or include unnecessary material.	Organization is inconsistent, and flaws are apparent.	Evidence is uneven or incomplete; insufficient use of facts and details.	Ideas are unevenly conveyed, using overly-simplistic language; lack of domain-specific vocabulary.	Command of conventions is uneven.
1	The response may be confusing, unfocused; opinion not sufficiently supported.	Organization is poor or nonexistent.	Evidence is poor or nonexistent.	Ideas are conveyed in a vague, unclear, or confusing manner.	There is very little command of conventions.
0	The response shows no evidence of the ability to construct a coherent opinion essay using information from sources.				

Ⓒ Common Core State Standards

Writing 1. Use a combination of drawing, dictating, and writing to compose opinion pieces in which they tell a reader the topic or the name of the book they are writing about and state an opinion or preference about the topic or book (e.g., *My favorite book is...*).

Name_____

Write Like a Reporter
Argument

Student Prompt Look at all of the different ways to get to school in *This Is the Way We Go to School*. Write which way you think would be the most fun. Give reasons for your choice.

_____

_____

_____

_____

_____

_____

_____

_____

_____

Write Like a Reporter
Argument

> **Student Prompt, p. 170** Look at all of the different ways to get to school in *This Is the Way We Go to School*. Write which way you think would be the most fun. Give reasons for your choice.

Writing to Sources Tell children to look back at the story *This Is the Way We Go to School* and write about it. Help children remember that students get to school many different ways. Ask children to name all the ways the students get to school and make a list on the board. Tell them to write about which way would be the most fun. Remind children to use reasons to support their opinions.

Children's sentences should:

- write an opinion
- support the opinion
- demonstrate strong command of the conventions of standard written English

Ⓒ **Common Core State Standards**

Writing 1. Use a combination of drawing, dictating, and writing to compose opinion pieces in which they tell a reader the topic or the name of the book they are writing about and state an opinion or preference about the topic or book (e.g., *My favorite book is...*).

Name_____

Connect the Texts

Argument

Student Prompt Look at the pictures in *This Is the Way We Go to School*. Look at the pictures in "The Dragon Test." Tell how the pictures are the same and different. Which pictures do you like better?

_____

_____

_____

_____

_____

_____

_____

_____

_____

_____

_____

_____

_____

_____

_____

_____

Connect the Texts

Argument

> **Student Prompt, p. 172** Look at the pictures in *This Is the Way We Go to School*. Look at the pictures in "The Dragon Test." Tell how the pictures are the same and different. Which pictures do you like better?

Writing to Sources Tell children to study the pictures in *This Is the Way We Go to School* and "The Dragon Test" on pp. 130–131 in *My Skills Buddy.* Help them make a list on the board of how the pictures are the same and how the pictures are different. Tell children to write which pictures they like better. Remind children to use the similarities and differences list from the board to support their claims or opinions.

___					
4-point Argument Writing Rubric					
Score	**Statement of Purpose/Focus**	**Organization**	**Development of Evidence**	**Language and Vocabulary**	**Conventions**
4	Opinion is clearly conveyed and well supported; response is focused.	Organization is clear and effective, creating a sense of cohesion.	Evidence is thorough and persuasive, and includes facts and details.	Ideas are clearly and effectively conveyed, using precise language and/or domain-specific vocabulary.	Command of conventions is strongly demonstrated.
3	Opinion is clear, adequately supported; response is generally focused.	Organization is clear, though minor flaws may be present and some ideas may be disconnected.	Evidence is adequate and includes facts and details.	Ideas are adequately conveyed, using both precise and more general language; may include domain-specific vocabulary.	Command of conventions is sufficiently demonstrated.
2	Opinion is somewhat supported; response may lack focus or include unnecessary material.	Organization is inconsistent, and flaws are apparent.	Evidence is uneven or incomplete; insufficient use of facts and details.	Ideas are unevenly conveyed, using overly-simplistic language; lack of domain-specific vocabulary.	Command of conventions is uneven.
1	The response may be confusing, unfocused; opinion not sufficiently supported.	Organization is poor or nonexistent.	Evidence is poor or nonexistent.	Ideas are conveyed in a vague, unclear, or confusing manner.	There is very little command of conventions.
0	The response shows no evidence of the ability to construct a coherent opinion essay using information from sources.				

⊚ **Common Core State Standards**

Writing 1. Use a combination of drawing, dictating, and writing to compose opinion pieces in which they tell a reader the topic or the name of the book they are writing about and state an opinion or preference about the topic or book (e.g., *My favorite book is...*).

Prove It!
Persuasive Paragraph

Academic Vocabulary

A persuasive paragraph is a type of argument or persuasive writing. In persuasive writing, the writer tries to convince the reader to agree with the writer's opinion about a topic, issue, or text.

ELL

Introduce Genre Write the words *persuade* and *persuasive* on the board. Explain to children that these words describe anything that tries to convince people to think or act in a certain way. Tell children that in a persuasive paragraph the writer gives an opinion about something and tries to convince readers to agree with that opinion. Discuss with children the key features of a persuasive paragraph that appear on this page.

My Favorite Transportation

Persuasive Paragraph

In this unit, children have read examples of argument writing and have had the opportunity to write in this mode. Remind children of texts and writing tasks (such as Write Like a Reporter) in which they have encountered and practiced argument writing.

Key Features of a Persuasive Paragraph

- states the writer's opinion on a topic
- tries to influence the reader's opinion
- supports the opinion with reasons backed by facts and details from the text
- uses persuasive words such as *must* or *best*

Writing Task Overview

Each unit writing task provides children with an opportunity to write using information from a selection they are reading. To successfully complete the task, children must understand and interpret the selection and create their own written response.

My Favorite Transportation

Part 1: Children will reread a selection identified from this unit. They will then respond to this selection and discuss their written response with partners.

Part 2: Children will work individually to plan, write, and revise their own persuasive paragraph.

Scorable Products: evidence-based short response, persuasive paragraph

My Favorite Transportation: Writing Task – Short Response

Teacher Directions:

1. Introduce the Source Reread the following Big Book selection:

This Is the Way We Go to School

Explain to children that they will use the words and illustrations in the book to respond. Tell children that they will also write their own persuasive paragraphs that use information from the text.

2. Have children draw a picture of one form of transportation in *This Is the Way We Go to School.*

3. Using evidence from the text, have children write or dictate a description of the form of transportation they have chosen. Tell them to include a reason they like this form of transportation.

© Common Core State Standards

Writing 1. Use a combination of drawing, dictating, and writing to compose opinion pieces in which they tell a reader the topic or the name of the book they are writing about and state an opinion or preference about the topic or book (e.g., *My favorite book is …*)

Scoring Information

Use the following 2-point scoring rubric to evaluate children's answers to the evidence-based short response.

	Evaluation Rubric
2	The response: • demonstrates the ability to evaluate text and form an opinion about a form of transportation • includes specific details that make reference to the text
1	The response: • demonstrates a limited ability to evaluate text and form an opinion about a form of transportation • includes some details that make reference to the text
0	A response gets no credit if it shows no ability to evaluate text or includes no relevant details from the text.

Ⓒ **Common Core State Standards**

Writing 1. Use a combination of drawing, dictating, and writing to compose opinion pieces in which they tell a reader the topic or the name of the book they are writing about and state an opinion or preference about the topic or book (e.g., *My favorite book is …*)

My Favorite Transportation

Writing Task – Short Response

Draw a picture of two kinds of transportation from *This Is the Way We Go to School.*

Name _____

Write a sentence about the kind of transportation.
Tell why you like it.

_____

- -

_____

- -

_____

- -

_____

- -

_____

- -

_____

- -

_____

- -

_____

- -

_____

My Favorite Transportation: Writing Task – Persuasive Paragraph

Teacher Directions:

1. Have children draw a picture of two forms of transportation in the selection *This Is the Way We Go to School.*

2. Have children write or dictate a short paragraph that gives their opinion about the two forms of transportation. Have them tell which form of transportation is their favorite and include reasons why others should agree.

3. Scoring Information Use the scoring rubric on the next page to evaluate children's persuasive paragraphs.

© Common Core State Standards

Writing 1. Use a combination of drawing, dictating, and writing to compose opinion pieces in which they tell a reader the topic or the name of the book they are writing about and state an opinion or preference about the topic or book (e.g., *My favorite book is …*)

	Argument Writing Rubric				
Score	Statement of Purpose/Focus	Organization	Development of Evidence	Language and Vocabulary	Conventions
4	Paragraph clearly states and supports opinion.	Organization includes a clear opinion, strong reasons, and a concluding statement.	Evidence includes sufficient facts and details.	Persuasive words are effectively used.	Use of conventions is clearly shown
3	Paragraph adequately states and supports opinion.	Organization includes an opinion, reasons, and a concluding statement.	Evidence includes some facts and details.	Persuasive words are used.	Use of conventions is somewhat shown.
2	Paragraph somewhat states opinion; includes unnecessary details.	Organization lacks an opinion or conclusion; reasons are unclear.	Evidence does not include facts and details.	Few persuasive words are used.	Use of conventions is uneven.
1	Paragraph is confusing; opinion is not supported.	Organization lacks opinion, reasons, and conclusion.	Evidence is poor or nonexistent.	There is little or no use of persuasive words.	There is very little correct use of conventions.
0	The response shows no evidence of the ability to construct a coherent persuasive paragraph using information from sources				

Common Core State Standards

Writing 1. Use a combination of drawing, dictating, and writing to compose opinion pieces in which they tell a reader the topic or the name of the book they are writing about and state an opinion or preference about the topic or book (e.g., *My favorite book is* …)

My Favorite Transportation

Writing Task – Persuasive Paragraph

Persuasive Paragraph Prompt

Draw a picture of two kinds of transportation from *This Is the Way We Go to School.* Which kind is your favorite? Write a paragraph that tells why other people should agree with you.

_____

- -

_____

- -

_____

- -

_____

Name _____

My Favorite Transportation: Writing Task – Persuasive Paragraph

Teacher Directions:

1. Publish Explain to children that publishing their writing is the last step in the writing process. If time permits, have children look at one another's paragraphs and incorporate any comments their classmates have. Discuss different ways technology can be used to publish writing.

2. Present Children will now have the option to present their persuasive paragraphs. Have children read aloud their paragraphs to the class. Use the list below to offer children tips on listening and speaking.

While Listening to a Classmate...
- Listen carefully.
- Think of relevant questions.

While Speaking to Classmates...
- Speak clearly at an appropriate pace.
- Face the audience.

Things to Do Together...
- Build on others' ideas.
- Ask questions to check understanding.

© **Common Core State Standards**

Writing 1. Use a combination of drawing, dictating, and writing to compose opinion pieces in which they tell a reader the topic or the name of the book they are writing about and state an opinion or preference about the topic or book (e.g., *My favorite book is* …)

Unit 6 Putting It Together

Writing Focus: Narrative

Name_____

Write Like a Reporter
Narrative

Student Prompt Reread *Building with Dad.* Talk about some events in this story. Write about events that happen at the beginning, middle, and end.

_____

- -

_____

- -

_____

- -

_____

- -

_____

- -

_____

- -

_____

- -

_____

- -

_____

Write Like a Reporter
Narrative

Student Prompt, p. 186 Reread *Building with Dad*. Talk about some events in this story. Write about events that happen at the beginning, middle, and end.

Writing to Sources Tell children to look at the story *Building with Dad* and to write about some events in the order they happened. Have them look at pages 4–5 and read the text. Ask children what is happening here. Write their responses on chart paper under the heading *Beginning*. Then look at pages 22–23 and read the text. Ask children what is happening here. Write their responses on chart paper under the heading *Middle*. Repeat with pages 30–31 and the heading *End*. Have children use words from the chart to finish the sentence frames and tell about some events: *At the beginning of the story, ____. In the middle of the story, ____. At the end of the story, ____.*

Children's sentences should:

- include a sequence of events that reflects those in the text
- give details about the sequence of events
- demonstrate strong command of the conventions of standard written English

© Common Core State Standards

Writing 3. Use a combination of drawing, dictating, and writing to narrate a single event or several loosely linked events, tell about the events in the order in which they occurred, and provide a reaction to what happened.

Connect the Texts
Narrative

> **Student Prompt** Reread the steps to build the school in *Building with Dad.* Then listen to "Two Kinds of Homes" again. Think about what Native Americans must have had to do make a tipi. Write those steps in order.

_____

_____

_____

_____

_____

_____

_____

_____

_____

Connect the Texts
Narrative

Student Prompt, p. 188 Reread the steps to build the school in *Building with Dad.* Then listen to "Two Kinds of Homes" again. Think about what Native Americans must have had to do make a tipi. Write those steps in order.

Writing to Sources Review *Building with Dad* with the children. Discuss the process of constructing a building. Reread "Two Kinds of Homes" (Teacher's Edition, page 99) and have children look at the pictures on pages 30–31 in *My Skills Buddy.* Using the text, discuss the materials used in those homes and how the homes were made. Then have children write a narrative telling how they think a tipi was made.

4-point Narrative Writing Rubric					
Score	**Narrative Focus**	**Organization**	**Development of Narrative**	**Language and Vocabulary**	**Conventions**
4	Narrative is clearly focused and developed throughout.	Narrative has a well-developed, logical, easy-to-follow plot.	Narrative includes thorough and effective use of details, dialogue, and description.	Narrative uses precise, concrete sensory language as well as figurative language and/or domain-specific vocabulary.	Narrative has correct grammar, usage, spelling, capitalization, and punctuation.
3	Narrative is mostly focused and developed throughout.	Narrative has a plot, but there may be some lack of clarity and/or unrelated events.	Narrative includes adequate use of details, dialogue and description.	Narrative uses adequate sensory and figurative language and/or domain-specific vocabulary.	Narrative has a few errors but is completely understandable.
2	Narrative is somewhat developed but may occasionally lose focus.	Narrative's plot is difficult to follow, and ideas are not connected well.	Narrative includes only a few details, dialogues, and description.	Language in narrative is not precise or sensory; lacks domain-specific vocabulary.	Narrative has some errors in usage, grammar, spelling and/or punctuation.
1	Narrative may be confusing, unfocused, or too short.	Narrative has little or no apparent plot.	Narrative includes few or no details, dialogue or description.	Language in narrative is vague, unclear, or confusing.	Narrative is hard to follow because of frequent errors.
0	Narrative gets no credit if it does not demonstrate adequate command of narrative writing traits.				

© Common Core State Standards

Writing 3. Use a combination of drawing, dictating, and writing to narrate a single event or several loosely linked events, tell about the events in the order in which they occurred, and provide a reaction to what happened.

Name_____

Write Like a Reporter
Narrative

Student Prompt Reread *Old MacDonald had a Woodshop*. Use details from the words and pictures to tell about the characters. Write about each animal that comes into the woodshop.

Write Like a Reporter
Narrative

Student Prompt, p. 190 Reread *Old MacDonald had a Woodshop*. Use details from the words and pictures to tell about the characters. Write about each animal that comes into the woodshop.

Writing to Sources Tell children that they will be looking at the story *Old MacDonald had a Woodshop* and writing about it. Tell children that the characters in our story come to Old MacDonald's woodshop and use different tools, but the animals' names are never used. Have children retell the story, but this time they will write each animal's name. Look at pages 8–9. Ask children which animal comes into the woodshop first. Tell them to write that on chart paper. Then tell children to look at pages 10–11 and write a sentence about the goat. Continue with each animal as it appears, in order, in the story. Then have children complete the following sentence frames using information from the text, to retell the story: *First, ___ comes into the woodshop. Then ____ comes in. The third animal to come in is ____. The next animal is ____. The fifth animal to enter is ___. And the last animal is ____.*

Children's sentences should:

- provide a list of characters
- include the correct order in which they enter the woodshop
- demonstrate strong command of the conventions of standard written English

© Common Core State Standards

Writing 3. Use a combination of drawing, dictating, and writing to narrate a single event or several loosely linked events, tell about the events in the order in which they occurred, and provide a reaction to what happened.

Name_____

Connect the Texts
Narrative

Student Prompt Read about make-believe animals in *Old MacDonald had a Woodshop*. Review the lullaby "Sleep, Baby, Sleep." Look at the pictures of Old MacDonald and the mother and describe each character. Write a description of the characters.

_____

- -

_____

- -

_____

- -

_____

- -

_____

- -

_____

- -

_____

- -

_____

Connect the Texts
Narrative

Student Prompt, p. 192 Read about make-believe animals in *Old MacDonald had a Woodshop*. Review the lullaby "Sleep, Baby, Sleep." Look at the pictures of Old MacDonald and the mother and describe each character. Write a description of the characters.

Writing to Sources Review *Old MacDonald had a Woodshop* and "Sleep, Baby, Sleep" with the children. Tell children to look at the pictures of Old MacDonald on pages 6–7. Ask children to think of phrases that describe Old MacDonald, such as *has white fur, wears an apron with flowers,* and *wears glasses.* Write them on chart paper under the heading *Old MacDonald*. Then do the same with the mother on pages 50–51 in *My Skills Buddy*. Encourage children to use color words as they describe the mother, such as *wears a blue dress, wears a white apron,* and *has long brown hair.* Then have children choose from the descriptive phrases and write two sentences that describe each character.

		4-point Narrative Writing Rubric			
Score	Narrative Focus	Organization	Development of Narrative	Language and Vocabulary	Conventions
4	Narrative is clearly focused and developed throughout.	Narrative has a well-developed, logical, easy-to-follow plot.	Narrative includes thorough and effective use of details, dialogue, and description.	Narrative uses precise, concrete sensory language as well as figurative language and/or domain-specific vocabulary.	Narrative has correct grammar, usage, spelling, capitalization, and punctuation.
3	Narrative is mostly focused and developed throughout.	Narrative has a plot, but there may be some lack of clarity and/or unrelated events.	Narrative includes adequate use of details, dialogue and description.	Narrative uses adequate sensory and figurative language and/or domain-specific vocabulary.	Narrative has a few errors but is completely understandable.
2	Narrative is somewhat developed but may occasionally lose focus.	Narrative's plot is difficult to follow, and ideas are not connected well.	Narrative includes only a few details, dialogues, and description.	Language in narrative is not precise or sensory; lacks domain-specific vocabulary.	Narrative has some errors in usage, grammar, spelling and/or punctuation.
1	Narrative may be confusing, unfocused, or too short.	Narrative has little or no apparent plot.	Narrative includes few or no details, dialogue or description.	Language in narrative is vague, unclear, or confusing.	Narrative is hard to follow because of frequent errors.
0	Narrative gets no credit if it does not demonstrate adequate command of narrative writing traits.				

Ⓒ **Common Core State Standards**

Writing 3. Use a combination of drawing, dictating, and writing to narrate a single event or several loosely linked events, tell about the events in the order in which they occurred, and provide a reaction to what happened.

Write Like a Reporter
Narrative

> **Student Prompt** Look at pages 4 and 5 in *Building Beavers.* Talk about where beavers live and what they need to build a house. Write about the setting.

_____

_____

_____

_____

_____

_____

_____

_____

_____

Write Like a Reporter
Narrative

> **Student Prompt, p. 194** Look at pages 4 and 5 in *Building Beavers.* Talk about where beavers live and what they need to build a house. Write about the setting.

Writing to Sources Have children look at pages 4–5 of *Building Beavers* and read the text. Explain that this is a story about real beavers and these pages show where the beavers live, or the setting. Explain to the children that the beaver is building an underwater lodge. Tell children to write about the setting. Children can use this sentence frame as a starter: *The setting of the story is* _____. Remind them to give details from the text about where the beavers live.

Children's sentences should:
- provide a setting and character
- use details to elaborate
- demonstrate strong command of the conventions of standard written English

© **Common Core State Standards**

Writing 3. Use a combination of drawing, dictating, and writing to narrate a single event or several loosely linked events, tell about the events in the order in which they occurred, and provide a reaction to what happened.

Connect the Texts
Narrative

Student Prompt Review where the beavers in *Building Beavers* live. Look at "The Milkmaid and Her Pail." Where does the milkmaid live? Write about where the beavers and the milkmaid live.

_____

_____

_____

_____

_____

_____

_____

_____

_____

_____

_____

_____

_____

_____

Connect the Texts
Narrative

Student Prompt, p. 196 Review where the beavers in *Building Beavers* live. Look at "The Milkmaid and Her Pail." Where does the milkmaid live? Write about where the beavers and the milkmaid live.

Writing to Sources Tell children to review where the beavers live in *Building Beavers*. Read "The Milkmaid and Her Pail" to children. Tell them to look at the pictures. Ask children where the beavers live and where the milkmaid lives. Tell the children to write sentences about where the characters live, or the setting. Children can use these sentence frames: *The beaver lives in ____. The milkmaid lives ____.*

		4-point Narrative Writing Rubric			
Score	**Narrative Focus**	**Organization**	**Development of Narrative**	**Language and Vocabulary**	**Conventions**
4	Narrative is clearly focused and developed throughout.	Narrative has a well-developed, logical, easy-to-follow plot.	Narrative includes thorough and effective use of details, dialogue, and description.	Narrative uses precise, concrete sensory language as well as figurative language and/or domain-specific vocabulary.	Narrative has correct grammar, usage, spelling, capitalization, and punctuation.
3	Narrative is mostly focused and developed throughout.	Narrative has a plot, but there may be some lack of clarity and/or unrelated events.	Narrative includes adequate use of details, dialogue and description.	Narrative uses adequate sensory and figurative language and/or domain-specific vocabulary.	Narrative has a few errors but is completely understandable.
2	Narrative is somewhat developed but may occasionally lose focus.	Narrative's plot is difficult to follow, and ideas are not connected well.	Narrative includes only a few details, dialogues, and description.	Language in narrative is not precise or sensory; lacks domain-specific vocabulary.	Narrative has some errors in usage, grammar, spelling and/or punctuation.
1	Narrative may be confusing, unfocused, or too short.	Narrative has little or no apparent plot.	Narrative includes few or no details, dialogue or description.	Language in narrative is vague, unclear, or confusing.	Narrative is hard to follow because of frequent errors.
0	Narrative gets no credit if it does not demonstrate adequate command of narrative writing traits.				

Ⓒ Common Core State Standards

Writing 3. Use a combination of drawing, dictating, and writing to narrate a single event or several loosely linked events, tell about the events in the order in which they occurred, and provide a reaction to what happened.

Write Like a Reporter
Narrative

Student Prompt Look at the text and the pictures in *Alistair and Kip's Great Adventure.* Read the last sentence in the story. Write a new adventure for Alistair and Kip.

_____

_____

_____

_____

_____

_____

_____

_____

_____

_____

_____

_____

Write Like a Reporter
Narrative

> **Student Prompt, p. 198 Student Prompt** Look at the text and the pictures in *Alistair and Kip's Great Adventure*. Read the last sentence in the story. Write a new adventure for Alistair and Kip.

Writing to Sources Reread the text and have children look at the pictures in *Alistair and Kip's Great Adventure*. Read the last sentence of the story: "Tomorrow let's build an airplane!" Have children begin a new adventure for Alistair and Kip, either in their airplane or doing some other adventurous activity. Children can begin with this sentence if they need a starter: *Kip wants to do something new!*

Children's sentences should:
- provide the characters
- tell a logical sequence of events
- demonstrate strong command of the conventions of standard written English

Ⓒ **Common Core State Standards**

Writing 3. Use a combination of drawing, dictating, and writing to narrate a single event or several loosely linked events, tell about the events in the order in which they occurred, and provide a reaction to what happened.

Connect the Texts

Narrative

> **Student Prompt** Look at *Alistair and Kip's Great Adventure*. Retell the story in your own words. Look at "Going to the Library." Retell the story in your own words. Write an adventure that Alistair and Kip might have with Taneesha.

_____

_____

_____

_____

_____

_____

_____

_____

_____

_____

Connect the Texts
Narrative

> **Student Prompt, p. 200** Look at *Alistair and Kip's Great Adventure*. Retell the story in your own words. Look at "Going to the Library." Retell the story in your own words. Write an adventure that Alistair and Kip might have with Taneesha.

Writing to Sources Using the text and illustrations, have children to look at the sequence of events in *Alistair and Kip's Great Adventure*. Ask them to retell the story in their own words. Tell children to look at the sequence of events in "Going to the Library" on pp. 90–91 in *My Skills Buddy*. Ask them to retell the story in their own words. Tell children to think about what might happen if Alistair and Kip were going to the library with Taneesha. Have children study the map. Ask where they think Alistair and Kip might want to stop. Write about an adventure they might have with Taneesha.

4-point Narrative Writing Rubric					
Score	**Narrative Focus**	**Organization**	**Development of Narrative**	**Language and Vocabulary**	**Conventions**
4	Narrative is clearly focused and developed throughout.	Narrative has a well-developed, logical, easy-to-follow plot.	Narrative includes thorough and effective use of details, dialogue, and description.	Narrative uses precise, concrete sensory language as well as figurative language and/or domain-specific vocabulary.	Narrative has correct grammar, usage, spelling, capitalization, and punctuation.
3	Narrative is mostly focused and developed throughout.	Narrative has a plot, but there may be some lack of clarity and/or unrelated events.	Narrative includes adequate use of details, dialogue and description.	Narrative uses adequate sensory and figurative language and/or domain-specific vocabulary.	Narrative has a few errors but is completely understandable.
2	Narrative is somewhat developed but may occasionally lose focus.	Narrative's plot is difficult to follow, and ideas are not connected well.	Narrative includes only a few details, dialogues, and description.	Language in narrative is not precise or sensory; lacks domain-specific vocabulary.	Narrative has some errors in usage, grammar, spelling and/or punctuation.
1	Narrative may be confusing, unfocused, or too short.	Narrative has little or no apparent plot.	Narrative includes few or no details, dialogue or description.	Language in narrative is vague, unclear, or confusing.	Narrative is hard to follow because of frequent errors.
0	Narrative gets no credit if it does not demonstrate adequate command of narrative writing traits.				

ⓒ **Common Core State Standards**

Writing 3. Use a combination of drawing, dictating, and writing to narrate a single event or several loosely linked events, tell about the events in the order in which they occurred, and provide a reaction to what happened.

Name_____

Write Like a Reporter

Narrative

> **Student Prompt** Look at the text and the pictures on pages 12, 13, 14, and 15. Choose one of the characters and write how that worker helped build Tony's house.

_____

_____

_____

_____

_____

_____

_____

_____

_____

_____

_____

_____

_____

_____

_____

_____

Write Like a Reporter
Narrative

> **Student Prompt, p. 202** Look at the text and the pictures on pages 12, 13, 14, and 15. Choose one of the characters and write how that worker helped build Tony's house.

Writing to Sources Tell children to look back at *The House That Tony Lives In* and write about it. Tell children to look at pages 12–13 and 14–15. Ask children to identify who the characters are. Using the text and illustrations, ask children to tell about the job that the characters are doing and why it is important. Children can use this sentence frame to begin their story: *I am a _____, and I used _____ to help build Tony's house.* Remind children to use words to show the order in which things are done.

Children's sentences should:

- tell about a character
- use details to describe the character
- follow a sequence
- demonstrate strong command of the conventions of standard written English

ⓒ **Common Core State Standards**

Writing 3. Use a combination of drawing, dictating, and writing to narrate a single event or several loosely linked events, tell about the events in the order in which they occurred, and provide a reaction to what happened.

Name_____

Connect the Texts
Narrative

Student Prompt Review *The House That Tony Lives In.* All of the workers do a good job. Look at "Juan Bobo." Juan does not do a good job. Look at pages 16 and 17 of *The House That Tony Lives In.* Write a story about what might happen if Juan Bobo is a mover.

Connect the Texts
Narrative

Student Prompt Review *The House That Tony Lives In*. All of the workers do a good job. Look at "Juan Bobo." Juan does not do a good job. Look at pages 16 and 17 of *The House That Tony Lives In*. Write a story about what might happen if Juan Bobo is a mover.

Writing to Sources Tell children to look at *The House That Tony Lives In*. Ask children if they think that the movers are doing a good job working on the house. Tell children to look at "Juan Bobo." Using the pictures as evidence, ask children if they think Juan Bobo does a good job helping his mother. Ask children to look at pages 16–17 of *The House That Tony Lives In* and to write about what might happen if Juan Bobo is one of the movers. Children might start their narrative with a sentence like this: *Juan Bobo is on the first day of his job as a mover.*

Score	Narrative Focus	Organization	Development of Narrative	Language and Vocabulary	Conventions
4	Narrative is clearly focused and developed throughout.	Narrative has a well-developed, logical, easy-to-follow plot.	Narrative includes thorough and effective use of details, dialogue, and description.	Narrative uses precise, concrete sensory language as well as figurative language and/or domain-specific vocabulary.	Narrative has correct grammar, usage, spelling, capitalization, and punctuation.
3	Narrative is mostly focused and developed throughout.	Narrative has a plot, but there may be some lack of clarity and/or unrelated events.	Narrative includes adequate use of details, dialogue and description.	Narrative uses adequate sensory and figurative language and/or domain-specific vocabulary.	Narrative has a few errors but is completely understandable.
2	Narrative is somewhat developed but may occasionally lose focus.	Narrative's plot is difficult to follow, and ideas are not connected well.	Narrative includes only a few details, dialogues, and description.	Language in narrative is not precise or sensory; lacks domain-specific vocabulary.	Narrative has some errors in usage, grammar, spelling and/or punctuation.
1	Narrative may be confusing, unfocused, or too short.	Narrative has little or no apparent plot.	Narrative includes few or no details, dialogue or description.	Language in narrative is vague, unclear, or confusing.	Narrative is hard to follow because of frequent errors.
0	Narrative gets no credit if it does not demonstrate adequate command of narrative writing traits.				

4-point Narrative Writing Rubric

Ⓒ **Common Core State Standards**

Writing 3. Use a combination of drawing, dictating, and writing to narrate a single event or several loosely linked events, tell about the events in the order in which they occurred, and provide a reaction to what happened.

Name_____

Write Like a Reporter
Narrative

Student Prompt Look at pages 16 and 17 in *Ants and Their Nests.* Describe how ants build their nests.

_____

- -

_____

- -

_____

- -

_____

- -

_____

- -

_____

- -

_____

- -

_____

Write Like a Reporter
Narrative

> **Student Prompt** Look at pages 16 and 17 in *Ants and Their Nests.* Describe how ants build their nests.

Writing to Sources Reread *Ants and Their Nests* with children. Using the text as evidence, ask children to describe the ants' nests. Make a list of their ideas. Tell children to write a description of how the ants' build their nests.

Children's sentences should:

- provide a setting and a character
- describe the sequence of actions
- demonstrate strong command of the conventions of standard written English

Writing 3. Use a combination of drawing, dictating, and writing to narrate a single event or several loosely linked events, tell about the events in the order in which they occurred, and provide a reaction to what happened.

Connect the Texts
Narrative

Student Prompt Think about what you learned about ants in *Ants and Their Nests*. Listen to "A Man at a Restaurant in Crewe" again. Write a funny poem about ants.

_____

_____

_____

_____

_____

_____

_____

_____

_____

_____

_____

_____

_____

_____

Connect the Texts
Narrative

Student Prompt, p. 208 Think about what you learned about ants in *Ants and Their Nests.* Listen to "A Man at a Restaurant in Crewe" again. Write a funny poem about ants.

Writing to Sources Using the text, discuss with children what they learned about ants in *Ants and Their Nests.* Reread "A Man at a Restaurant in Crewe" (Teacher's Edition, p. 495). Ask children what makes the poem funny. Tell children to write a funny poem about ants. Have children suggest rhyming words and list them on chart paper. They can use these in their poems. If children need help, provide a first line for a two-line poem, such as: *The ant jumped off the sugar cube* or *Once there was a silly ant.*

			4-point Narrative Writing Rubric		
Score	**Narrative Focus**	**Organization**	**Development of Narrative**	**Language and Vocabulary**	**Conventions**
4	Narrative is clearly focused and developed throughout.	Narrative has a well-developed, logical, easy-to-follow plot.	Narrative includes thorough and effective use of details, dialogue, and description.	Narrative uses precise, concrete sensory language as well as figurative language and/or domain-specific vocabulary.	Narrative has correct grammar, usage, spelling, capitalization, and punctuation.
3	Narrative is mostly focused and developed throughout.	Narrative has a plot, but there may be some lack of clarity and/or unrelated events.	Narrative includes adequate use of details, dialogue and description.	Narrative uses adequate sensory and figurative language and/or domain-specific vocabulary.	Narrative has a few errors but is completely understandable.
2	Narrative is somewhat developed but may occasionally lose focus.	Narrative's plot is difficult to follow, and ideas are not connected well.	Narrative includes only a few details, dialogues, and description.	Language in narrative is not precise or sensory; lacks domain-specific vocabulary.	Narrative has some errors in usage, grammar, spelling and/or punctuation.
1	Narrative may be confusing, unfocused, or too short.	Narrative has little or no apparent plot.	Narrative includes few or no details, dialogue or description.	Language in narrative is vague, unclear, or confusing.	Narrative is hard to follow because of frequent errors.
0	Narrative gets no credit if it does not demonstrate adequate command of narrative writing traits.				

© Common Core State Standards

Writing 3. Use a combination of drawing, dictating, and writing to narrate a single event or several loosely linked events, tell about the events in the order in which they occurred, and provide a reaction to what happened.

Prove It!
Personal Narrative

Academic Vocabulary

A personal narrative is a story that the writer tells about something that happened in his or her own life.

ELL

Introduce Genre Write *story* on the board. Ask children to tell what a story is and to give examples. Explain that a story tells about someone or something. Then write *personal narrative*. Tell children that a personal narrative is a story about the writer. Discuss with children the key features of a personal narrative that appear on this page.

What I Build

Personal Narrative

In this unit, children have read examples of narrative writing and have had the opportunity to write in this mode. Remind children of texts and writing tasks (such as Write Like a Reporter) in which they have encountered and practiced narrative writing.

Key Features of a Personal Narrative
- tells about an interesting event in your life
- gives details that help readers understand the event
- uses the words *I*, *me*, and *my*
- uses words to show the sequence
- has a beginning, middle, and end

Writing Task Overview

Each unit writing task provides children with an opportunity to write using information from a selection they are reading. To successfully complete the task, children must understand and interpret the selection and create their own response.

What I Build

Part 1: Children will read the selection identified from this unit. They will then respond to this selection and discuss their written response with partners.

Part 2: Children will work individually to plan, write, and revise their own personal narrative.

Scorable Products: evidence-based short response, personal narrative

What I Build: Writing Task – Short Response

Teacher Directions:

1. Introduce the Source Reread the following Big Book selection:

Building with Dad

Explain to children that they will use the words and illustrations in the book in their response. Tell children that they will also write their own personal narratives that use information from the text.

2. Have children draw a picture of one character in *Building with Dad*.

3. Using evidence from the text, have children write or dictate an event from the story involving the character they have chosen. Tell them to use the words *I, me,* and *my* as they write.

Ⓒ **Common Core State Standards**

Writing 3. Use a combination of drawing, dictating, and writing to narrate a single event or several loosely linked events, tell about the events in the order in which they occurred, and provide a reaction to what happened.

Scoring Information

Use the following 2-point scoring rubric to evaluate children's answers to the evidence-based short response.

Analysis Rubric	
2	The response: • demonstrates the ability to analyze story details in order to describe an event using the words *I, me,* and *my* • includes specific details that make reference to the text
1	The response: • demonstrates a limited ability to analyze story details in order to describe an event using the words *I, me,* and *my* • includes some details that make reference to the text
0	A response gets no credit if it shows no ability to analyze story details or includes no relevant details from the text.

Ⓒ Common Core State Standards

Writing 3. Use a combination of drawing, dictating, and writing to narrate a single event or several loosely linked events, tell about the events in the order in which they occurred, and provide a reaction to what happened.

What I Build

Writing Task – Short Response

Draw a picture of a character from *Building with Dad.*

Name _____

Write a sentence about the character.

_____

- -

_____

_____

- -

_____

_____

- -

_____

_____

- -

_____

_____

- -

_____

_____

- -

_____

_____

- -

_____

What I Build: Writing Task – Personal Narrative

Teacher Directions:

1. Have children draw a picture of something they have built.

2. Have children write or dictate a narrative telling how they built the object. Tell them to use language from *Building with Dad*, such as *I, me,* and *my,* to help them as they write.

3. **Scoring Information** Use the scoring rubric on the next page to evaluate children's personal narratives.

Ⓒ **Common Core State Standards**

Writing 3. Use a combination of drawing, dictating, and writing to narrate a single event or several loosely linked events, tell about the events in the order in which they occurred, and provide a reaction to what happened.

	Narrative Writing Rubric				
Score	**Narrative Focus**	**Organization**	**Development of Narrative**	**Language and Vocabulary**	**Conventions**
4	Narrative is correctly focused on the person.	Narrative has an easy-to-follow plot.	Narrative includes effective use of details.	Narrative uses sensory language.	Narrative has correct use of conventions.
3	Narrative is mostly focused on the person.	Narrative has an event (plot).	Narrative includes adequate use of details.	Narrative uses some sensory language.	Narrative has a few errors but is completely understandable.
2	Narrative is somewhat focused on the person.	Narrative's event (plot) is confusing.	Narrative includes only a few details.	Language in narrative is not sensory.	Narrative has some errors in basic conventions.
1	Narrative may be confusing or unfocused.	Narrative has little or no apparent plot.	Narrative includes few or no details.	Language in narrative is vague or confusing.	Narrative is hard to follow because of frequent errors.
0	Narrative gets no credit if it does not demonstrate adequate command of narrative writing traits.				

© Common Core State Standards

Writing 3. Use a combination of drawing, dictating, and writing to narrate a single event or several loosely linked events, tell about the events in the order in which they occurred, and provide a reaction to what happened.

Name _____

What I Build

Writing Task – Personal Narrative

Personal Narrative Prompt

Draw a picture of something you have built. Write a story about how you built it. Your story should use words from *Building with Dad.*

Name _____

What I Build: Writing Task – Personal Narrative

Teacher Directions:

1. Publish Explain to children that publishing their writing is the last step in the writing process. If time permits, have children review one another's narratives and incorporate any comments their classmates have. Discuss different ways technology can be used to publish writing.

2. Present Children will now have the option to present their personal narratives. Have children tell about their narratives in front of the class. Use the list below to offer children some tips on listening and speaking.

While Listening to a Classmate...
- Face the speaker to listen attentively.
- Think about what the speaker says.

While Speaking to Classmates...
- Have good posture and eye contact.
- Speak at an appropriate pace.

Things to Do Together...
- Ask and answer questions with detail.
- Build on each other's ideas.

Ⓒ **Common Core State Standards**

Writing 3. Use a combination of drawing, dictating, and writing to narrate a single event or several loosely linked events, tell about the events in the order in which they occurred, and provide a reaction to what happened.

More Connect the Texts

More Connect the Texts
Opinion Poster

Objectives

- Identify the characteristics of an opinion poster.
- Write a caption for your opinion poster using one fact.
- Evaluate your writing.
- Revise and publish your writing with a picture.

 Common Core State Standards

Writing 1. Use a combination of drawing, dictating, and writing to compose opinion pieces in which they tell a reader the topic or the name of the book they are writing about and state an opinion or preference about the topic or book (e.g., *My favorite book is . . .*). **Writing 8.** With guidance and support from adults, recall information from experiences or gather information from provided sources to answer a question.

STEP 1 Read Like a Writer

Review the key features of an opinion poster listed below. Respond to any questions children might have.

Key Features of an Opinion Poster

- States the topic of the poster
- States the writer's opinion about the topic
- Includes a picture to help illustrate the writer's opinion
- Uses correct sentence conventions

Choose an opinion piece or persuasive text that children have already read to model key features. Display the model for children to see and point out each of the key features you have discussed.

STEP 2 Organize Your Ideas

Writing Prompt Look back at *Smash! Crash!* and *Dig Dig Digging.* Both stories introduce you to a variety of trucks. Which truck in these stories is your favorite? Create a poster for the truck. Write a title for your poster. Draw a picture of your favorite truck below the title. Write a sentence to tell which truck you like best below your picture.

Think Aloud Let's talk about which trucks you like. Look back at both stories to see the illustrations and the words in the texts. We can copy the names of the trucks from the texts.

Guided Writing Draw a sample poster on the board. At the top of the poster, draw a write-on line for the topic of the poster, for example, "My Favorite Truck" or "The Dump Truck." Write this sentence frame on the board: *My favorite truck is _____.* Explain that this sentence will tell children's opinion.

STEP 3 Draft Your Writing

Have children review the stories and pick their favorite truck. They can copy the sentence frame and the names of the trucks onto their papers. Have them practice writing each letter in a word from left to right. Remind them to capitalize the first word in the sentence and end with a period.

Think Aloud One of the best ways to share your opinion about something is to give lots of details about it, either with words or pictures. This helps convince others to like it as much as you do.

Getting Started Tell children to draw their pictures toward the top of their papers, leaving room for the title above and the sentence frame below.

STEP 4 Evaluate Your Writing

Display the checklist below and have children use it to evaluate their opinion posters. Circulate around the room and confer with individual children.

✓ Did I write the topic or title of the poster at the top?
✓ Did I state my opinion clearly?
✓ Did I draw a picture to help illustrate my opinion?
✓ Did I use correct sentence conventions?

Help children set goals and make a plan for improving in areas where their writing needs help.

STEP 5 Revise and Publish

Help children understand the conventions of writing a title and a sentence. Show them how to make a capital letter for each word of the title. Have them carefully write their sentences under the picture.

Publishing Children can hang their posters around the room. If time permits, have children share their posters and talk about their reasons for their choice.

More Connect the Texts
Opinion Letter

STEP 1 Read Like a Writer

Review the key features of an opinion letter listed below. Respond to any questions children might have.

Key Features of an Opinion Letter

- States the writer's opinion about a topic
- Supports the opinion with a reason, a fact, or an example
- Uses persuasive words such as *most* and *best*
- Uses correct letter format and conventions

Choose an opinion piece or persuasive text that children have already read to model key features. Display the model for children to see and point out each of the key features you have discussed.

STEP 2 Organize Your Ideas

Writing Prompt Look back at "Grandma's Garden" (Teacher's Edition, p. 331) and *Miss Bindergarten Takes a Field Trip with Kindergarten.* Tommy and Grandma and the kindergarten class go to a lot of places. Pick a place that you like the best and write a letter to a friend in your class to explain why you like this place.

Think Aloud Decide on the opinion you will state in your letter. Then decide what fact, detail, or example from the stories you will use to support your opinion. You may wish to fill in a chart before you begin writing to help you.

Guided Writing Display a chart with two boxes as an example. Show children where to write their opinion in the first box using the sentence frame *I like the _____ the best.* In the second box, they will write an idea that supports their opinion using the sentence frame *I like it because _____.* Explain to children that when they write, they will first state their opinion and then follow it with a reason. Discuss with children why they like the places they do. Write words and phrases from children's responses on the board so they can copy them into the sentence frames.

STEP 3 Draft Your Writing

Have children fill out their charts. Encourage them to review the texts to find additional words to help them write their reasons. Talk about the form of a letter. Draw an example on the board. Tell children to start the letter with *Dear* _____, (put their friend's name on the line and then insert a comma). On the next line down, show children where they will begin writing their opinion and reason in the sentence frames. Show children how they would add a closing to their letter, such as *Sincerely,* followed by their name.

Think Aloud One of the best ways to share opinions is to use facts and details to support, or help prove, your opinion. You can find facts and details by reviewing "Grandma's Garden" and *Miss Bindergarten Takes a Field Trip with Kindergarten.* Look at the illustrations in *Miss Bindergarten Takes a Field Trip with Kindergarten.* Look for details that will help with your reasons.

Getting Started Tell children to begin writing their opinion letters using their charts to keep them on track. First, have them write a greeting to their friend. Then guide them in writing their opinion sentence and their reason sentence. Have them practice writing their letters and sentences before they write the final letter. Explain sentence conventions of starting a sentence with a capital letter and ending it with a period.

STEP 4 Evaluate Your Writing

Display the checklist below and have children use it to evaluate their opinion letters. Circulate around the room and confer with individual children.

   ✓ Did I state my opinion clearly?
   ✓ Does my reason support my opinion?
   ✓ Did I use persuasive words to make my writing more convincing?
   ✓ Did I use correct letter format and conventions?

Help children set goals and make a plan for improving in areas where their writing needs help.

STEP 5 Revise and Publish

Help children follow through with their plans for revision. If time permits, have children draw a picture to accompany their letter.

Publishing Children can publish their opinion letter by presenting it to the person to whom it is addressed.

Persuasive Advertisement

Objectives

- Identify the characteristics of a persuasive advertisement.
- Write a persuasive ad, using facts and supporting details.
- Use persuasive words and phrases such as *most*, *best*, *exciting*, and *must see*.
- Evaluate your writing.
- Revise and publish your writing.

 Common Core State Standards

Writing 1. Use a combination of drawing, dictating, and writing to compose opinion pieces in which they tell a reader the topic or the name of the book they are writing about and state an opinion or preference about the topic or book (e.g., *My favorite book is . . .*). **Writing 8.** With guidance and support from adults, recall information from experiences or gather information from provided sources to answer a question.

STEP 1 Read Like a Writer

Review the key features of a persuasive advertisement listed below. Respond to any questions children might have.

Key Features of a Persuasive Advertisement
- States the writer's opinion about a topic
- Includes a title
- Tries to influence the attitudes or actions of people
- Supports the opinion with a reason, a fact, or an example
- Uses persuasive words and phrases such as *most*, *best*, and *must see*
- Organizes reasons in order of importance

Choose an opinion piece or persuasive text that children have already read to model key features. Display the model for children to see and point out each of the key features you have discussed.

STEP 2 Organize Your Ideas

Writing Prompt Look back at *We Are So Proud!* and "Working in the Kitchen" (Teacher's Edition, p. 539). One story describes a wonderful parade. The other describes making a treat in the kitchen. Create a persuasive advertisement for a parade. Invite people to come to see your parade and offer them baked treats as they watch so that they will want to come. Use facts and details from both stories to make people want, or persuade them, to come. Include words and phrases such as *important, wonderful,* and *must see* in your persuasive advertisement.

Think Aloud It is important to organize our ideas. We want to persuade people to come to our parade. We will find exciting details from each text to include in the advertisement. We will make a list to refer to as we write. Each statement should be short and descriptive.

Guided Writing First, review with children *We Are So Proud!* and write a list of important details on the board. (great music, a beautiful float, our nation's flag, "honor our great nation") After reviewing "Working in the Kitchen," add *delicious apple muffins* or another treat to your list.

STEP 3 Draft Your Writing

Have children plan a drawing for the ad. Guide them in writing a title across the top, such as "Come to the Big Parade." Have children list details to persuade people to come. Be sure to mention a treat. Use persuasive words such as "You *must see* this parade," or "Try the *best* muffins." Remind children about the conventions of sentences, for example, using a capital letter to begin the sentence and a period to end it. You may want to explain the use of the exclamation mark for emphasis at the end of their statements.

Think Aloud This advertisement should excite people and remind them to come to your parade. Look back at *We Are So Proud!* and "Working in the Kitchen" for phrases that provide details and descriptions you can use in your ad.

Getting Started Tell children to write a title and draw an illustration on their papers. Guide them in planning the placement of their details below the artwork. Encourage them to think of an exciting concluding statement.

STEP 4 Evaluate Your Writing

Display the checklist below and have children use it to evaluate their persuasive advertisements. Circulate around the room and confer with individual children.

✓ Did I include a title for the advertisement?

✓ Did I use facts and supporting details?

✓ Did I try to influence the attitudes or actions of people?

✓ Did I use persuasive words and phrases such as *most*, *best, exciting,* and *must see?*

✓ Did I use capital letters and punctuation correctly?

Help children set goals and make a plan for improving in areas where their writing needs help.

STEP 5 Revise and Publish

Help children follow through with their plans for revision. If time permits, have children trade persuasive advertisements and offer one another suggestions for how to improve the writing.

Publishing Children can publish their persuasive advertisements by posting them on a bulletin board for classmates and others to read.

More Connect the Texts
Opinion Poster

Objectives

- Identify the characteristics of an opinion poster.
- Write a caption for your opinion poster using one or two facts to support your opinion.
- Evaluate your writing.
- Revise and publish your writing with a picture.

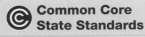 **Common Core State Standards**

Writing 1. Use a combination of drawing, dictating, and writing to compose opinion pieces in which they tell a reader the topic or the name of the book they are writing about and state an opinion or preference about the topic or book (e.g., *My favorite book is . . .*). **Writing 8.** With guidance and support from adults, recall information from experiences or gather information from provided sources to answer a question.

STEP 1 Read Like a Writer

Review the key features of an opinion poster listed below. Respond to any questions children might have.

Key Features of an Opinion Poster
- States the topic of the poster
- States the writer's opinion about the topic
- Lists one or two reasons to support the writer's opinion
- Includes a picture to help illustrate the writer's opinion
- Uses correct sentence conventions

Choose an opinion piece or persuasive text that children have already read to model key features. Display the model for children to see and point out each of the key features you have discussed.

STEP 2 Organize Your Ideas

Writing Prompt Look back at "A Growing Foal" (Teacher's Edition, p. 225) and *Animal Babies in Grasslands.* Both stories introduce you to baby animals. Write a sentence to tell which animal you like best. Then you can list a reason to support your opinion. Draw a picture of your favorite animal baby.

Think Aloud Let's talk about which animal baby you like best. Look back at both selections and review the photographs and the words in the texts. We can copy the names of the animals from the texts. Think about why you like the animal baby. Make a list of your reasons.

Guided Writing Create a sample poster on the board. At the top of the poster, draw a write-on line for the topic of the poster, for example, "The Foal" or "The Zebra." Write this sentence frame on the board: *My favorite baby animal is _____.* Explain that this sentence tells children's opinion. Then guide children in listing one or two reasons why they like the animal. Encourage them to use details from the text to help clarify their supporting reasons.

STEP 3 Draft Your Writing

Have children review the stories and pick their favorite animal baby. Tell them to copy the sentence frame and the name of their favorite animals onto their papers. Have them practice writing each letter in a word from left to right. Remind children to capitalize the first word in the sentence and end it with a period.

Think Aloud Once you have selected your favorite animal, practice writing your sentences and your title. We will practice writing carefully so each letter is clear and there is the proper space between each word.

Getting Started Tell children to draw their pictures toward the top of their poster, leaving room for a title above and the sentences below.

STEP 4 Evaluate Your Writing

Display the checklist below and have children use it to evaluate their opinion posters. Circulate around the room and confer with individual children.

✓ Did I write the topic or title of the poster at the top?

✓ Did I state my opinion clearly?

✓ Did I draw a picture to help illustrate my opinion?

✓ Did I list one or two reasons to support my opinion?

✓ Did I use correct sentence conventions?

Help children set goals and make a plan for improving in areas where their writing needs help.

STEP 5 Revise and Publish

Help children understand the conventions of writing a title and a sentence. Show them how to make a capital letter for each word of the title. Have them carefully write their sentences under the picture.

Publishing Children can hang their posters around the room. If time permits, have children share their posters and talk about the reasons for their choice.

More Connect the Texts
Opinion Paragraph

Objectives

- Identify the characteristics of an opinion paragraph.
- Write an opinion paragraph, using an opinion and one or two supporting reasons.
- Evaluate your writing.
- Revise and publish your writing.

 Common Core State Standards

Writing 1. Use a combination of drawing, dictating, and writing to compose opinion pieces in which they tell a reader the topic or the name of the book they are writing about and state an opinion or preference about the topic or book (e.g., *My favorite book is . . .*). **Writing 8.** With guidance and support from adults, recall information from experiences or gather information from provided sources to answer a question.

STEP 1 Read Like a Writer

Review the key features of an opinion paragraph listed below. Respond to any questions children might have.

Key Features of an Opinion Paragraph
- States the writer's opinion about a topic
- Supports the opinion with a reason, a fact, or an example
- Uses persuasive words such as *most* and *best*
- Uses correct sentence and punctuation conventions

Choose an opinion piece or persuasive text that children have already read to model key features. Display the model for children to see and point out each of the key features you have discussed.

STEP 2 Organize Your Ideas

Writing Prompt Look back at the story *Jack and the Beanstalk* and the Read Aloud "Jack and the Beanstalk" (Teacher's Edition, p. 527). The first story has lines that rhyme. Decide which version you like best. Write your opinion. Use details from both stories to help you finish the following sentences: *I like the version of* Jack and the Beanstalk *(that rhymed or did not rhyme) the best. I like it because* _____. *I also like* _____.

Think Aloud Decide which story you like best. What facts, details, or examples from the texts will you use to support your opinion? You may wish to fill in a chart before you begin writing.

Guided Writing Display a chart with three or four boxes as an example. Show children where to write their opinion in the first box in the sentence frame *I like the version of* Jack and the Beanstalk *(that rhymed or did not rhyme) the best.* In the second and third boxes have them write reasons that support their opinion in the sentence frames *I like it because* _____ and *I also like* _____. Explain that when they write, they will first state their opinion and then follow with their reasons.

STEP 3 Draft Your Writing

Have children fill out their charts. They can review the texts to find words to help them write their reasons.

Think Aloud One of the best ways to share opinions is to use facts and details to support your opinion. You can find facts and details by reviewing the stories. You also may find details in the pictures that will help support your reasons.

Getting Started Tell children to begin writing their opinion paragraph using their charts to keep them on track. They can include descriptive details they find in the texts. Have them practice writing their letters, words, and sentences before they write the final version. Explain the sentence conventions of starting a sentence with a capital letter and ending it with a period. Guide them in adding a title above the paragraph.

STEP 4 Evaluate Your Writing

Display the checklist below and have children use it to evaluate their opinion paragraphs. Circulate around the room and confer with individual children.

- ✓ Did I state my opinion clearly?
- ✓ Do my reasons support my opinion?
- ✓ Did I use persuasive words such as *more* and *best* to make my writing more convincing?
- ✓ Did I use correct sentence conventions?

Help children set goals and make a plan for improving in areas where their writing needs help.

STEP 5 Revise and Publish

Help children follow through with their plans for revision. If time permits, have children draw a picture to accompany their opinion paragraphs.

Publishing Children can publish their paragraphs by presenting them orally to partners.

More Connect the Texts
Persuasive Letter/Invitation

STEP 1 Read Like a Writer

Review the key features of a persuasive letter listed below. Respond to any questions children might have.

Key Features of a Persuasive Letter

- States the writer's opinion about a topic
- Supports the opinion or purpose with reasons, facts, or examples
- Uses persuasive words such as *most* and *best*
- Uses correct letter format and conventions

Choose an opinion piece or persuasive text that children have already read to model key features. Display the model for children to see and point out each of the key features you have discussed.

STEP 2 Organize Your Ideas

Writing Prompt Look back at *Bear Snores On* and *A Bed for the Winter*. In the first story, all the animals are having such a good time in Bear's cave. Write a party invitation from Hare in *Bear Snores On* to the dormouse in *A Bed for the Winter*. What will you say to her to make her want to come to the party?

Think Aloud Let's talk about the fun the animals have in Bear's cave. I will make a list on the board. Think about what would interest the dormouse—there would be good food, singing, dancing, and storytelling. Are these things that you like to do? Let's think of words that would make it sound exciting: *great food, funny stories, lots of fun.*

Guided Writing Have children share what they like about parties. Write their statements on the board. Explain that exclamation marks are used at the end of sentences to show excitement. Compose an invitation with two or three sentences describing what a good time the dormouse will have, for example, *Please come to our party. It will be fun!*

STEP 3 Draft Your Writing

Talk to children about organizing their invitations with the most important reasons first. Remind them of the key features of a persuasive letter/invitation.

Think Aloud One of the best ways to help people accept, or say yes to, an invitation is to use exciting words to describe how much fun they will have. Do our invitations sound exciting? Remember, we must make the invitation sound very exciting to persuade the dormouse to come.

Getting Started Have children carefully copy the phrases on the board. Remind them to insert spaces between words and end sentences with the correct punctuation. They can begin their invitations with *Dear Dormouse,* and then sign their names at the bottom. Have children decorate the invitation with a picture.

STEP 4 Evaluate Your Writing

Display the checklist below and have children use it to evaluate their persuasive letter/invitation. Circulate around the room and confer with individual children.

✓ Did I state my purpose clearly?

✓ Do my reasons support my purpose?

✓ Did I use persuasive words to make my invitation more exciting and convincing?

✓ Did I use correct letter format and sentence conventions?

Help children set goals and make a plan for improving in areas where their writing needs help.

STEP 5 Revise and Publish

Help children follow through with their plans for revision. If time permits, have them take turns sharing their invitations orally in small groups.

Publishing Children can publish their invitations by posting them around the room or making a class invitation book.

More Connect the Texts
Opinion Paragraph

Objectives

- Identify the characteristics of an opinion paragraph.
- Write an opinion paragraph, using an opinion and one or two supporting reasons.
- Evaluate your writing.
- Revise and publish your writing.

 Common Core State Standards

Writing 1. Use a combination of drawing, dictating, and writing to compose opinion pieces in which they tell a reader the topic or the name of the book they are writing about and state an opinion or preference about the topic or book (e.g., *My favorite book is . . .*). **Writing 8.** With guidance and support from adults, recall information from experiences or gather information from provided sources to answer a question.

STEP 1 Read Like a Writer

Review the key features of an opinion paragraph listed below. Respond to any questions children might have.

Key Features of an Opinion Paragraph

- States the writer's opinion about a topic
- Supports the opinion with reasons, facts, or examples
- Uses persuasive words such as *most* and *best*
- Uses correct sentence and punctuation conventions

Choose an opinion piece or persuasive text that children have already read to model key features. Display the model for children to see and point out each of the key features you have discussed.

STEP 2 Organize Your Ideas

Writing Prompt Look back at *Flowers* and "The Ant and the Grasshopper" (Teacher's Edition, p. 97). Write an opinion paragraph about why it is or is not important to take care of plants.

Think Aloud Decide on the opinion you will state in your paragraph. "The Ant and the Grasshopper" talks about using plants for food. *Flowers* describes how plants grow, how beautiful they are, and how we use them for food. Decide what facts, details, or reasons from the texts you will use to support your opinion. You may wish to make a list before you begin writing.

Guided Writing Discuss with children what their opinions are. Write them on the board with some details they mention. On their papers, they will first state an opinion on why it is or is not important to take care of plants. Then they can list the facts and reasons to support their arguments.

STEP 3 Draft Your Writing

Have children start the writing of their opinion paragraphs. Have them use their lists of facts and reasons to support their opinions.

Think Aloud Look back at *Flowers* and "The Ant and the Grasshopper" to find reasons to support your opinion. You can list your reasons with the most important reason first. Use details to make your writing interesting. Use persuasive words such as *important, necessary, better,* and *best.*

Getting Started Have children write their opinion paragraphs. They should use their lists to develop two or three reasons. Remind them to use details from both texts to make the writing interesting. Children should restate their opinion at the end to make a conclusion for their argument.

STEP 4 Evaluate Your Writing

Display the checklist below and have children use it to evaluate their opinion paragraphs. Circulate around the room and confer with individual children.

- ✓ Did I state my opinion clearly?
- ✓ Do my facts and reasons support my opinion?
- ✓ Did I use persuasive words to make my writing more convincing?
- ✓ Did I use correct sentence conventions?

Help children set goals and make a plan for improving in areas where their writing needs help.

STEP 5 Revise and Publish

Help children follow through with their plans for revision.

Publishing Children can publish their opinion paragraphs by sharing them with another classmate or presenting them to the class.

Opinion Poster

Objectives

- Identify the characteristics of an opinion poster.
- Write a caption for your opinion poster, using one fact and one supporting detail.
- Evaluate your writing.
- Revise and publish your writing with a picture.

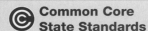 Common Core State Standards

Writing 1. Use a combination of drawing, dictating, and writing to compose opinion pieces in which they tell a reader the topic or the name of the book they are writing about and state an opinion or preference about the topic or book (e.g., *My favorite book is . . .*).

STEP 1 Read Like a Writer

Review the key features of an opinion poster listed below. Respond to any questions children might have.

Key Features of an Opinion Poster

- States the writer's opinion about a topic
- Supports the opinion with a reason, a fact, or an example
- Uses persuasive words, such as *most* and *best*
- Includes a picture to help illustrate the writer's opinion
- Uses correct sentence conventions

Choose an opinion poster that children have already seen to model key features. Display the poster for children to see and point out the key features you have discussed.

STEP 2 Organize Your Ideas

Writing Prompt Look back at *Little Panda* and "Lions" (Teacher's Edition, p. 593). Both texts discuss real animals. Do you have a favorite? Write a sentence to tell which animal you like best. Then write a sentence to give a reason why you like that animal. Draw a picture of your favorite animal at the top of the poster.

Think Aloud Think about your reasons for choosing a favorite animal. I will write some of the words and phrases that you suggest on the board so you can copy them later and write them on your poster.

Guided Writing Write this sentence frame on the board: *My favorite animal is ____.* Explain that this is their opinion. Then write another sentence frame: *I like this animal the best because ____.* Explain that the words after *because* provide their reason. If children have more than one reason for choosing an animal as a favorite, tell them to put the most important reason first.

STEP 3 Draft Your Writing

Have children review the selections, look at the illustrations, and choose their favorite animal. They can copy some of the words from the selections and from the board. Remind children that they write the letters in a word from left to right.

Think Aloud When you state the reason for your opinion about a favorite animal, it is important to use facts or details. You can find facts and details by reviewing *Little Panda* and "Lions." You can also look at books, articles, and Web sites to find additional facts about your favorite animal.

Getting Started Tell children to draw their picture at the top of the paper, leaving enough room to write their two sentences below it.

STEP 4 Evaluate Your Writing

Display the checklist below and have children use it to evaluate their opinion posters. Circulate around the room and confer with individual children.

> ✓ Did I state my opinion clearly?
> ✓ Does my reason support my opinion?
> ✓ Did I use correct sentence conventions?

Help children set goals and make a plan for improving in areas where their writing needs help.

STEP 5 Revise and Publish

Help children follow through with their plans for revision and carefully write their sentences under the picture.

Publishing Children can display their posters around the room. If time permits, have children share their posters and talk about their reasons for their choice.

More Connect the Texts
Opinion Text

 Common Core State Standards

Writing 1. Use a combination of drawing, dictating, and writing to compose opinion pieces in which they tell a reader the topic or the name of the book they are writing about and state an opinion or preference about the topic or book (e.g., *My favorite book is . . .*).

STEP 1 Read Like a Writer

Review the key features of an opinion text listed below. Respond to any questions children might have.

Key Features of an Opinion Text
- States the writer's opinion about a topic
- Supports the opinion with a reason, fact, or an example
- Uses persuasive words such as *most* and *best*
- Uses correct sentence and punctuation conventions

Choose an opinion piece or persuasive text that children have already read to model key features. Display the model for children to see and point out each of the key features you have discussed.

STEP 2 Organize Your Ideas

Writing Prompt Look back at "How Coyote Helped People" (Teacher's Edition, p. 495) and *The Lion and the Mouse.* Both stories are about characters that help someone else. Who do you think was braver? Choose from the coyote that brought fire to people or the mouse that helped the lion escape from the net. Write a sentence to tell which character you think was braver.

Think Aloud We know that both characters are brave. Let's talk about why you think one character was braver than the other. I'll write some of your ideas on the board.

Guided Writing Write this sentence frame on the board: *I think that _____ was braver than _____.* Explain that the character that they think is braver is written first. Now children will write a reason for their opinion with this frame: *The reason I think that _____ was braver than _____ is because _____.* If children have more than one reason, tell them to put their reasons in order with the most important first.

STEP 3 Draft Your Writing

Have children review the stories and pick the character that they think was braver. They can copy some of the words from the stories and copy other words from the board. Have them practice writing each letter in a word from left to right.

Think Aloud The best way to support your opinion is to use facts and details from the stories. You can find facts and details by reviewing "How Coyote Helped People" and *The Lion and the Mouse.* Look at the illustrations. You may find details that will help with your reasons.

Getting Started Tell children to begin writing their opinion text using their sentence frames to keep them on track. First, they will write their opinion. Then they will decide which facts or reasons to use. They can practice writing their sentences before they write the final opinion text.

STEP 4 Evaluate Your Writing

Display the checklist below and have children use it to evaluate their opinion texts. Circulate around the room and confer with individual children.

  ✓ Did I state my opinion clearly?
  ✓ Do my reasons support my opinion?
  ✓ Did I use correct sentence and punctuation conventions?

Help children set goals and make a plan for improving in areas where their writing needs help.

STEP 5 Revise and Publish

Help children follow through with their plans for revision. If time permits, have children draw a picture of the character they chose.

Publishing Children can publish their text by compiling them in a book.

More Connect the Texts
Opinion Paragraph

Objectives

- Identify the characteristics of an opinion paragraph.
- Write an opinion paragraph, using an opinion and one or two supporting details.
- Evaluate your writing.
- Revise and publish your writing.

 **Common Core State Standards**

Writing 1. Use a combination of drawing, dictating, and writing to compose opinion pieces in which they tell a reader the topic or the name of the book they are writing about and state an opinion or preference about the topic or book (e.g., *My favorite book is . . .*).

STEP 1 Read Like a Writer

Review the key features of an opinion paragraph listed below. Respond to any questions children might have.

Key Features of an Opinion Paragraph

- States the writer's opinion about a topic
- Supports the opinion with reasons, facts, or examples
- Uses descriptive words to make writing more convincing
- Often organizes reasons in order of importance
- Uses correct paragraph format and conventions

Choose an opinion piece or persuasive text that children have already read to model key features. Display the model for children to see and point out each of the key features you have discussed.

STEP 2 Organize Your Ideas

Writing Prompt Look back at *George Washington Visits* and *Then and Now*. These selections are about people and events from long ago. Think about how life in our country was different a long time ago. Would you like to visit the past? Decide if you would like to visit the past and write about it. Tell why you would like to visit the past or why you would not.

Think Aloud Your ideas will be more convincing if they are well organized. Decide on the opinion, or claim, you will state in your paragraph. Then decide what facts, reasons, and examples from the texts you will use to support your opinion. Let's brainstorm some words and sentences on the board before we get started.

Guided Writing Write this sentence frame on the board: *I (would, would not) like to visit the past.* Explain that this is their opinion. Then have children write a reason for their opinion. *I (would, would not) like to visit the past because _____.* If children have more than one reason, tell them to put their reasons in order with the most important first. Continue to help children think of descriptive words and phrases to use in their paragraphs. Write them on the board for children to copy.

STEP 3 Draft Your Writing

Have children review facts and details from *George Washington Visits* and *Then and Now.* Then have them decide whether they would like to visit America a long time ago. They can copy some of the words from the selections and from the board. Have them practice writing each letter in a word from left to right.

Think Aloud The best way to support your opinion is to use facts, reasons, or examples. You can find facts and details by reviewing *George Washington Visits* and *Then and Now*. Look at the photographs and illustrations. You may find details that will help support your feelings.

Getting Started Tell children to begin writing their opinion paragraph using the sentence frames from the board to keep them on track. First, they will write their opinion. Then they will use facts, reasons, and examples for support. They can practice writing their sentences before they write the final paragraph.

STEP 4 Evaluate Your Writing

Display the checklist below and have children use it to evaluate their opinion paragraphs. Circulate around the room and confer with individual children.

- ✓ Did I state my opinion clearly?
- ✓ Do my reasons, facts, or examples support my opinion?
- ✓ Did I use descriptive words to make my writing more convincing?
- ✓ Did I place my most important details first?
- ✓ Did I use correct paragraph format and conventions?

Help children set goals and make a plan for improving in areas where their writing needs help.

STEP 5 Revise and Publish

Help children follow through with their plans for revision. If time permits, have children draw a picture of themselves living in the past.

Publishing Children can publish their opinion paragraphs by compiling them in a book to share.

More Connect the Texts
Opinion Letter

STEP 1 Read Like a Writer

Review the key features of an opinion letter listed below. Respond to any questions children might have.

Key Features of an Opinion Letter

- States the writer's opinion about a topic
- Supports the opinion with reasons, facts, and examples
- Uses descriptive words to make writing more convincing
- Uses correct letter format and conventions

Choose an opinion letter or persuasive text that children have already read to model key features. Display the model for children to see and point out each of the key features you have discussed.

STEP 2 Organize Your Ideas

Writing Prompt Review *Rooster's Off to See the World* and "The Evening Is Coming" (Teacher's Edition, p. 95). The first selection is a fantasy. The second is a lullaby. Each selection ends in the evening, or at night, when the characters go to sleep. Think about your favorite part of evening. Write a letter to a classmate. Tell why that part of the evening is your favorite.

Think Aloud Your ideas will be more convincing if they are well organized. Decide on the opinion, or claim, you will state in your letter. Then decide what facts, details, and examples from the texts you will use to support your opinion. Let's brainstorm ideas on the board before you begin writing to organize your thoughts.

Guided Writing Write children's ideas on the board so they can copy them. Show children how to write their opinion using the sentence frame *My favorite part of the evening is _____.* Then they can write one or two ideas that support their opinion using the sentence frame *The _____ is my favorite part of evening because _____.* (If children have more than one reason, tell them to put their reasons in order with the most important reason first.)

STEP 3 Draft Your Writing

Have children use the sentence frames and ideas from the board to write an opinion letter. Remind them of the key features of an opinion letter. Tell them to write *Dear _____,* (with their classmate's name on the line and a comma after it). On the next line down, they will begin their letter with their opinion. After writing their opinion and reasons, children may write *Sincerely,* followed by their name.

Think Aloud Using descriptive words is a great way to make a convincing argument. Review *Rooster's Off to See the World* and "The Evening Is Coming" and think about the words the authors use to write about the evening.

Getting Started Tell children to write their opinion letter using the sentence frames and ideas from the board to keep them on track. First, they will give their opinion. Then they will use facts, reasons, and examples for support. Remind them to use words that describe the evening and their feelings. They can practice writing their letters and sentences before they write the final letter.

STEP 4 Evaluate Your Writing

Display the checklist below and have children use it to evaluate their opinion letters. Circulate around the room and confer with individual children.

✓ Did I state my opinion clearly?

✓ Do my reasons, facts, or examples support my opinion?

✓ Did I use descriptive words to make my writing more convincing?

✓ Did I use correct letter format and conventions?

Help children set goals and make a plan for improving in areas where their writing needs help.

STEP 5 Revise and Publish

Help children follow through with their plans for revision. If time permits, have children draw a picture to accompany their letter.

Publishing Children can publish their letter by presenting it to the person to whom it is addressed.

More Connect the Texts
Review

STEP 1 Read Like a Writer

Review the key features of a review listed below. Respond to any questions children might have.

Key Features of a Review
- Introduces the selection
- Gives an opinion about the selection
- Gives reasons that support the opinion
- Often urges others to read the selection

Model key features by selecting a review children have already read or using another piece of argument writing. Display the model for children to see and point out each of the key features you have discussed.

STEP 2 Organize Your Ideas

Writing Prompt Review *Goldilocks and the Three Bears* and "How the Fly Saved the River" (Teacher's Edition, p. 399). Both texts are about animals who scare away a character. Write a review that tells what you like or dislike about each selection. Tell why a person should or should not read these stories. Support your review with details from the texts.

Think Aloud Your ideas will be more convincing if they are well organized. Decide on the opinion, or claim, you will state in your review. Then decide what facts, details, and examples from the texts you will use to support your opinion. Let's brainstorm ideas on the board before you begin writing to organize your thoughts.

Guided Writing Write children's ideas on the board so they can copy them. Show children how to write their opinion using the sentence frame *I liked it when _____.* Then they can write one or two ideas that support their opinion using the sentence frame *I liked this part because _____.* (If children have more than one reason, tell them to put their reasons in order with the most important reason first.) Continue with frames for parts children did not like. *I did not like it when _____. I did not like this part because _____.*

STEP 3 Draft Your Writing

Have children use the sentence frames and ideas from the board to write a review of the two stories. Remind them of the key features of a review.

Think Aloud Your review will be better if you include details from both stories. We can look back at the stories to decide which parts we like or don't like.

Getting Started Tell children to begin writing their reviews using the sentence frames to keep them on track. Remind them to begin with a statement of opinion and follow with a reason and examples from the texts. Emphasize the importance of using complete sentences and punctuation. Encourage children to include a drawing of their favorite character from the stories. They can practice writing their letters and sentences before they write the final review.

STEP 4 Evaluate Your Writing

Display the checklist below and have children use it to evaluate their review. Circulate around the room and confer with individual children.

✓ Did I introduce my topic at the beginning?
✓ Did I state my opinion clearly?
✓ Do my reasons support my opinion?
✓ Did I urge others to read the texts?
✓ Did I include a drawing?

Help children set goals and make a plan for improving in areas where their writing needs help.

STEP 5 Revise and Publish

Help children follow through with their plans for revision. If time permits, have children draw a picture to accompany their review.

Publishing Children can publish their reviews by presenting them in small groups.

More Connect the Texts
Advertisement

Objectives

- Identify characteristics of an advertisement.
- Write a title for your advertisement.
- Write a caption for your advertisement.
- Evaluate your writing.
- Revise and publish your writing with a picture.

 Common Core State Standards

Writing 1. Use a combination of drawing, dictating, and writing to compose opinion pieces in which they tell a reader the topic or the name of the book they are writing about and state an opinion or preference about the topic or book (e.g., *My favorite book is . . .*).

STEP 1 Read Like a Writer

Review the key features of an advertisement listed below. Respond to any questions children might have.

Key Features of an Advertisement
- Includes a title for the advertisement
- States an opinion about the topic
- Supports the opinion with a reason, fact, or example
- Uses persuasive words to influence people
- Often includes pictures or illustrations
- Uses correct sentence format and conventions

Choose an advertisement or persuasive text that children have already read to model key features. Display the model for children to see and point out each of the key features you have discussed.

STEP 2 Organize Your Ideas

Writing Prompt Reread *If You Could Go to Antarctica* and *Abuela.* These selections are about two very different places. Antarctica is cold and beautiful. Rosalba lives in a big, colorful city. Think about which place you would like to live. Use the texts and photographs to form your opinion. Create an advertisement to make others want to live in this place.

Think Aloud Organize each part of your advertisement. Think of where on the advertisement you could put a photograph or draw a picture. Think of a title for your advertisement. It can be the name of the place you choose to live. Decide on the opinion, or claim, you will state in your advertisement. Then decide what facts, details, and examples from the selections you will use to support your opinion. Let's brainstorm some sentences and phrases we can use in our advertisements.

Guided Writing Write these sentence frames on the board. *The place I would like to live is _____.* Explain that this is their opinion. Now they will write a reason for their opinion. (If children have more than one reason, tell them to put their reasons in order with the most important reason first.) *It is the best because _____.* Last, they will write a sentence to influence or persuade people. *Everyone should live in _____ because _____.* (If children have more than one reason, tell them to put their reasons in order with the most important reason first.)

STEP 3 Draft Your Writing

Have children use the sentence frames to write an advertisement. Remind them of the key features of an advertisement.

Think Aloud Use facts and details about a place to support your decision. You can find facts and details by reviewing *If You Could Go to Antarctica* and *Abuela.* You can also use the library to find books and electronic information about your topic.

Getting Started Tell children to add photographs or pictures to their paper, leaving enough room to write their sentences.

STEP 4 Evaluate Your Writing

Display the checklist below and have children use it to evaluate their advertisements. Circulate around the room and confer with individual children.

✓ Did I title my advertisement?

✓ Did I state my opinion clearly?

✓ Do my reasons support my opinion?

✓ Did I use persuasive words to influence people?

✓ Did I include a picture or photograph?

✓ Did I use correct sentence format and conventions?

Help children set goals and make a plan for improving in areas where their writing needs help.

STEP 5 Revise and Publish

Help children follow through with their plans for revision and carefully write their sentences under the picture.

Publishing Children can publish their advertisements by presenting them to the class and placing them on display.

More Connect the Texts
Persuasive Statement

Objectives

- Identify the characteristics of a persuasive statement.
- Plan and write a persuasive statement.
- Use persuasive words and reasons to convince readers.
- Evaluate your writing.
- Revise and publish your writing.

 Common Core State Standards

Writing 1. Use a combination of drawing, dictating, and writing to compose opinion pieces in which they tell a reader the topic or the name of the book they are writing about and state an opinion or preference about the topic or book (e.g., *My favorite book is . . .*).

STEP 1 Read Like a Writer

Review the key features of a persuasive statement listed below. Respond to any questions children might have.

Key Features of a Persuasive Statement

- Makes a clear statement of opinion
- Uses reasons, facts, and examples to make a point
- Uses persuasive words, such as *must* or *best*
- Often organizes facts in order of importance
- Uses proper conventions

Choose a persuasive text or opinion piece that children have already read to model key features. Display the model for children to see and point out each of the key features you have discussed.

STEP 2 Organize Your Ideas

Writing Prompt Review *Abuela* and "The Statue of Liberty" (Teacher's Edition, p. 599). Abuela and Rosalba fly around the head of the Statue of Liberty. They both like the statue. Why do you think they like the Statue of Liberty? Why do you think so many people visit the statue? Write a sentence to tell why you think people like the Statue of Liberty. Then write a sentence telling why you think people should visit the statue.

Think Aloud Your ideas will be more convincing if they are well organized. Decide on the opinion, or claim, you will state in your paragraph. Then decide what facts, reasons, and examples from the texts you will use to support your opinion. Let's brainstorm some words and sentences on the board before we get started.

Guided Writing Write this model sentence on the board: *I think people like the Statue of Liberty.* Explain that this is an opinion. In this sentence frame, they will write a reason for their opinion: *I think people like the statue because _____.* Then write *The Statue of Liberty is a great place to visit because _____.* If children have more than one reason, tell them to put their reasons in order with the most important first. Help children think of persuasive words to add, such as *best, most,* and *important.*

STEP 3 Draft Your Writing

Have children use the model sentence and sentence frames to write a persuasive statement. Remind them of the key features of a persuasive statement.

Think Aloud The best way to support your opinion is to use facts, reasons, or examples. You can find facts and details by reviewing *Abuela* and "The Statue of Liberty." Look at the illustrations. You may find details that will help with your reasons.

Getting Started Tell children to begin writing their persuasive statements using the model sentence and sentence frames as a guide. First they will write their opinion. Then they will use facts, reasons, and examples from the two selections for support. They can practice writing their letters and sentences before they write the final paragraph.

STEP 4 Evaluate Your Writing

Display the checklist below and have children use it to evaluate their persuasive statements. Circulate around the room and confer with individual children.

  ✓ Did I state my opinion clearly?
  ✓ Do my reasons, facts, or examples support my opinion?
  ✓ Did I use persuasive words to make my writing more convincing?
  ✓ Did I use facts in order of importance?
  ✓ Did I use proper conventions?

Help children set goals and make a plan for improving in areas where their writing needs help.

STEP 5 Revise and Publish

Help children follow through with their plans for revision. If time permits, have children draw a picture of the Statue of Liberty.

Publishing Children can publish their persuasive statements by presenting them to the class and compiling them in a book to share.

More Connect the Texts
Opinion Letter

Objectives

- Identify the characteristics of an opinion letter.
- Write an opinion letter, using an opinion and one or two supporting details.
- Evaluate your writing.
- Revise and publish your writing.

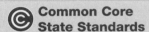 **Common Core State Standards**

Writing 1. Use a combination of drawing, dictating, and writing to compose opinion pieces in which they tell a reader the topic or the name of the book they are writing about and state an opinion or preference about the topic or book (e.g., *My favorite book is . . .*). **Writing 8.** With guidance and support from adults, recall information from experiences or gather information from provided sources to answer a question.

STEP 1 Read Like a Writer

Review the key features of an opinion letter listed below. Respond to any questions children might have.

Key Features of an Opinion Letter

- States the writer's opinion about a topic
- Supports the opinion with reasons, facts, and examples
- Often organizes reasons in order of importance
- Uses descriptive words to make writing more convincing
- Uses correct letter format and conventions

Choose an opinion piece or persuasive text that children have already heard or read to model key features. Display the model for children to see and point out each of the key features you have discussed.

STEP 2 Organize Your Ideas

Writing Prompt Look back at *Mayday! Mayday!* and *Trucks Roll!* Both texts discuss jobs: a Coast Guard rescuer and a truck driver. Pick which job you would like to do. Write a letter to a friend to explain why. Use evidence from both texts.

Think Aloud Your ideas will be more convincing if they are well organized. Decide on the opinion you will state in your letter. Then decide what facts, details, and examples from the texts you will use to support your opinion. Let's fill in a chart before you begin writing to organize your thoughts.

Guided Writing Display a chart with two or three boxes as an example. Show children how to write their opinion in the first box using the sentence frame *I want to be a _____, not a _____.* Then in the other boxes they can write one or two ideas that support their opinion using the sentence frame *I want to be a _____ because _____.* If children have more than one reason, tell them to put their reasons in order with the most important reason first.

STEP 3 Draft Your Writing

Have children use their charts to write an opinion letter. Remind them of the key features of an opinion letter. Tell them to write *Dear* _____, (with their friend's name on the line and a comma after it). On the next line down, they will begin their letter with their opinion. After writing their opinion and reasons, they may write *Sincerely,* and then their name.

Think Aloud The best way to support an opinion is to use facts and details. You can find facts and details by reviewing *Mayday! Mayday!* and *Trucks Roll!* You can also look at books, articles, and Web sites to find additional facts about the job you chose.

Getting Started Tell children to write their opinion letter using their chart to keep them on track. First they will state their opinion. Then they will give facts, reasons, and examples for support. They can practice writing their letters and sentences before they write the final letter.

STEP 4 Evaluate Your Writing

Display the checklist below and have children use it to evaluate their opinion letters. Circulate around the room and confer with individuals.

✓ Did I state my opinion clearly?

✓ Do my reasons, facts, or examples support my opinion?

✓ Did I put my reasons in an order that makes sense?

✓ Did I use descriptive words to make my writing more convincing?

✓ Did I use correct letter format and conventions?

Help children set goals and make a plan for improving in areas where their writing needs help.

STEP 5 Revise and Publish

Help children follow through with their plans for revision. If time permits, have children draw a picture to accompany their letter.

Publishing Children can publish their letter by presenting it to the person to whom it is addressed.

More Connect the Texts
Character Review

Objectives

- Identify the characteristics of a character review.
- Write a character review, using facts and supporting details.
- Evaluate your writing.
- Revise and publish your writing.

 Common Core State Standards

Writing 1. Use a combination of drawing, dictating, and writing to compose opinion pieces in which they tell a reader the topic or the name of the book they are writing about and state an opinion or preference about the topic or book (e.g., *My favorite book is . . .*). **Writing 8.** With guidance and support from adults, recall information from experiences or gather information from provided sources to answer a question.

STEP 1 Read Like a Writer

Review the key features of a character review listed below. Respond to any questions children might have.

Key Features of a Character Review

- Introduces the topic and states the writer's opinion about the topic
- Supports the opinion with reasons, facts, or examples
- Uses descriptive words to make writing more convincing
- Uses correct sentence format and conventions

Choose an opinion piece or persuasive text that children have already heard or read to model key features. Display the model for children to see and point out each of the key features you have discussed.

STEP 2 Organize Your Ideas

Writing Prompt Look back at "Queen of the Forest" (Teacher's Edition, p. 407) and "The Wind and the Sun" (Teacher's Edition, p. 203). The main characters in both stories trick and compete with each other to try and prove that they are the best at something. Which character's actions make him or her the biggest bully? Write a sentence to tell which character you choose. Then write a sentence to explain why you chose that character. Use evidence from both texts.

Think Aloud Your writing will be more persuasive if your ideas are organized. Decide what opinion you will state in your character review. Decide what the reasons for your opinion will be. Choose facts, details, and examples from the texts to support your reasons. Let's review each text and make lists of ideas and reasons before you begin writing.

Guided Writing Show children how to make a list of relevant information for the main character of each story. Write the name of the character and details of the character's actions, thoughts, and feelings that reveal what the character is like. Explain to children that when they write their character review, they will begin by briefly describing the characters. Then they will state their opinion about which character is the biggest bully. Finally, they will state their reasons in an order that makes sense.

STEP 3 Draft Your Writing

Have children use the lists on the board to write a character review. Remind them of the key features of a character review.

Think Aloud How can you persuade readers to agree with your opinion? Give them reasons, facts, and details that clearly support your opinion. Make lists of details about the main characters in "Queen of the Forest" and "The Wind and the Sun."

Getting Started Tell children to begin writing their character review using the lists from the board to keep them on track. Offer suggestions about how to organize their reasons, facts, and details. Brainstorm words and phrases they can use to make their writing more persuasive. Emphasize the importance of using correct grammar and complete sentences.

STEP 4 Evaluate Your Writing

Display the checklist below and have children use it to evaluate their character reviews. Circulate around the room and confer with individuals.

✓ Did I introduce my topic?

✓ Did I state my opinion clearly?

✓ Do my reasons, facts, or examples support my opinion?

✓ Did I use descriptive words to make my writing more persuasive?

✓ Did I use correct sentence format and conventions?

Help children set goals and make a plan for improving in areas where their writing needs help.

STEP 5 Revise and Publish

Help children follow through with their plans for revision. If time permits, have children draw a picture of the character they chose to accompany their paragraph.

Publishing Children can publish their character review by sharing it with their family.

Opinion Paragraph

Objectives

- Identify the characteristics of an opinion paragraph.
- Write an opinion paragraph, using an opinion and one or two supporting details.
- Evaluate your writing.
- Revise and publish your writing.

Ⓒ Common Core State Standards

Writing 1. Use a combination of drawing, dictating, and writing to compose opinion pieces in which they tell a reader the topic or the name of the book they are writing about and state an opinion or preference about the topic or book (e.g., *My favorite book is . . .*). **Writing 8.** With guidance and support from adults, recall information from experiences or gather information from provided sources to answer a question.

STEP 1 Read Like a Writer

Review the key features of an opinion paragraph listed below. Respond to any questions children might have.

Key Features of an Opinion Paragraph

- States the writer's opinion about a topic
- Supports the opinion with reasons, facts, or examples
- Often organizes reasons in order of importance
- Uses descriptive words to make writing more convincing
- Uses correct paragraph format and conventions

Choose an opinion piece or persuasive text that children have already heard or read to model key features. Display the model for children to see and point out each of the key features you have discussed.

STEP 2 Organize Your Ideas

Writing Prompt Look back at "Queen of the Forest" (Teacher's Edition, p. 407) and "The Dragon Test" (Teacher's Edition, p. 609). Both stories are about characters who want to be King or Queen. Who would make the best King or Queen? Would it be the tiger, the fox, the eldest son, the middle son, or the youngest son? Write a sentence to tell which character you choose. Then write a sentence to explain why you chose that character. Use evidence from both texts.

Think Aloud Your ideas will be more convincing if they are well organized. Decide on the opinion you will state in your paragraph. Then decide what facts, reasons, and examples from the texts you will use to support your opinion. Let's brainstorm some words and sentences on the board before we get started.

Guided Writing Write the following sentence frames on the board. _____ *would make the best King/Queen.* Explain to children that this sentence tells their opinion. Next, they will write a reason for their opinion. *I think _____ would make the best King/ Queen because _____.* If children have more than one reason, tell them to put their reasons in order with the most important first. Continue to help children think of descriptive words and phrases to use in their paragraphs. Write them on the board for children to copy.

STEP 3 Draft Your Writing

Have children review the stories and pick the character they think would make the best King or Queen. They can copy some of the words from the stories and from the board. Have them practice writing each letter in a word from left to right.

Think Aloud The best way to support your opinion is to use facts, reasons, or examples. You can find facts and details by reviewing "Queen of the Forest" and "The Dragon Test." Look at the illustrations. You may find details in them that you can use.

Getting Started Tell children to begin writing their opinion paragraph using the sentence frames from the board. First they will write their opinion. Then they will write facts, reasons, and examples for support. They can practice writing their letters and sentences before they write the final paragraph.

STEP 4 Evaluate Your Writing

Display the checklist below and have children use it to evaluate their opinion paragraphs. Circulate around the room and confer with individuals.

- ✓ Did I state my opinion clearly?
- ✓ Do my reasons, facts, or examples support my opinion?
- ✓ Did I put my reasons in an order that makes sense?
- ✓ Did I use descriptive words to make my writing more convincing?
- ✓ Did I use correct paragraph format and conventions?

Help children set goals and make a plan for improving in areas where their writing needs help.

STEP 5 Revise and Publish

Help children follow through with their plans for revision. If time permits, have children draw a picture of the character they chose wearing a crown.

Publishing Children can publish their opinion paragraph by showing their drawing to the class and reading aloud their paragraph.

More Connect the Texts
Advertisement

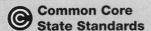
STEP 1 Read Like a Writer

Review the key features of an advertisement listed below. Respond to any questions children might have.

Key Features of an Advertisement

- Gives a title that tells the topic
- States an opinion about the topic
- Supports the opinion with a reason, fact, or example
- Uses persuasive words to try to make people think or act a certain way
- Often includes pictures or other graphics
- Uses correct sentence format and conventions

Choose an opinion piece or persuasive text that children have already heard or read to model key features. Display the model for children to see and point out each of the key features you have discussed.

STEP 2 Organize Your Ideas

Writing Prompt Look back at *On the Move!* and *This Is the Way We Go to School.* Both stories tell about people using different types of transportation. Which is the best type of transportation from the stories? Write a sentence that tells your opinion. Then write a sentence that gives a reason to support your opinion. Use facts and examples from the text. Persuade readers to use this type of transportation. Draw a picture of someone using your type of transportation at the top of the advertisement.

Think Aloud Your ideas will be more convincing if they are well organized. Think of a title for your advertisement. It can be the name of the type of transportation you chose. Decide on the opinion you will state in your advertisement. Then decide what facts, details, and examples from the stories you will use to support your opinion. Let's brainstorm some sentences and phrases we can use in our advertisements.

Guided Writing Write the following sentence frames on the board. *The best type of transportation is _____.* Explain to children that this sentence tells their opinion. Next, they will write a reason for their opinion. *It is the best because _____.* Last, they will write a sentence to persuade people to use that type of transportation. *Everyone should use _____ because _____.*

STEP 3 Draft Your Writing

Have children use the sentence frames to write an advertisement. Remind them of the key features of an advertisement.

Think Aloud The best way to support your opinion and persuade readers is to use facts and details. You can find facts and details by reviewing *On the Move!* and *This Is the Way We Go to School.* You can also look at books, articles, and Web sites to find additional facts about your topic.

Getting Started Tell children to draw their pictures at the top of their paper, leaving enough room to write their sentences.

STEP 4 Evaluate Your Writing

Display the checklist below and have children use it to evaluate their advertisements. Circulate around the room and confer with individuals.

- ✓ Did I include a title on my advertisement?
- ✓ Did I state my opinion clearly?
- ✓ Do my reasons support my opinion?
- ✓ Did I use persuasive words to try to get people to agree with me?
- ✓ Did I use correct sentence format and conventions?

Help children set goals and make a plan for improving in areas where their writing needs help.

STEP 5 Revise and Publish

Help children follow through with their plans for revision and carefully write their sentences under the picture.

Publishing Children can publish their advertisement by presenting it to the class and then posting it where people who use transportation can see it.

More Connect the Texts
Opinion Poster

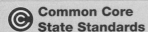

Common Core State Standards

Writing 1. Use a combination of drawing, dictating, and writing to compose opinion pieces in which they tell a reader the topic or the name of the book they are writing about and state an opinion or preference about the topic or book (e.g., *My favorite book is . . .*). **Writing 8.** With guidance and support from adults, recall information from experiences or gather information from provided sources to answer a question.

STEP 1 Read Like a Writer

Review the key features of an opinion poster listed below. Respond to any questions children might have.

Key Features of an Opinion Poster
- Has a title
- States an opinion about the topic
- Supports the opinion with a reason, fact, or example
- Uses descriptive words to make writing more convincing
- Often includes pictures or illustrations
- Uses correct poster format and conventions

Choose an opinion poster that children have already seen to model key features. Display the model for children and point out each of the key features you have discussed.

STEP 2 Organize Your Ideas

Writing Prompt Look back at *Building Beavers* and *Ants and Their Nests.* Both texts show how the animals build their homes, raise their young, and get their food. Which is your favorite animal? Write a sentence that includes an opinion about the animal. Then write a sentence that gives a reason from the text to support your opinion. Draw a picture of the animal.

Think Aloud Your ideas will be more convincing if they are well organized. Think of a title for your poster. It can be the name of the animal you chose as your favorite. Decide on the opinion, or claim, you will state on your poster. Then decide what facts, details, and examples from the texts you will use to support your opinion. Let's brainstorm some sentences and phrases you can use on your posters.

Guided Writing Write these sentence frames on the board: *My favorite animal is _____.* Explain that this is their opinion. Now they will write a reason for their opinion. *It is my favorite animal because _____.* (If children have more than one reason, tell them to put their reasons in order with the most important reason first.)

STEP 3 Draft Your Writing

Have children use the sentence frames to write their opinion. Remind them of the key features of an opinion poster.

Think Aloud The best way to support your opinion is to use facts and details. You can find facts and details by reviewing *Building Beavers* and *Ants and Their Nests*. You can also look at books, articles, and Web sites to find additional facts about your topic.

Getting Started Tell children to write their sentences at the top of their paper, leaving enough room to draw their pictures.

STEP 4 Evaluate Your Writing

Display the checklist below and have children use it to evaluate their opinion posters. Circulate around the room and confer with individual children.

✓ Did I make a title for my poster?

✓ Did I state my opinion clearly?

✓ Do my reasons support my opinion?

✓ Did I use descriptive words to make my writing more convincing?

✓ Did I use correct poster format and conventions?

Help children set goals and make a plan for improving in areas where their writing needs help.

STEP 5 Revise and Publish

Help children follow through with their plans for revision and carefully write their sentences above the picture.

Publishing Children can publish their poster by sharing it with their family.

More Connect the Texts
Persuasive Letter

 Common Core State Standards

Writing 1. Use a combination of drawing, dictating, and writing to compose opinion pieces in which they tell a reader the topic or the name of the book they are writing about and state an opinion or preference about the topic or book (e.g., *My favorite book is . . .*). **Writing 8.** With guidance and support from adults, recall information from experiences or gather information from provided sources to answer a question.

STEP 1 Read Like a Writer

Review the key features of a persuasive letter listed below. Respond to any questions children might have.

Key Features of a Persuasive Letter

- States the writer's opinion about a topic
- Supports the opinion with reasons, facts, and examples
- Uses persuasive words to influence the attitudes or actions of people
- Often organizes reasons in order of importance
- Uses correct letter formation and conventions

Choose an opinion piece or persuasive text that children have already read to model key features. Display the model for children to see and point out each of the key features you have discussed.

STEP 2 Organize Your Ideas

Writing Prompt Look back at *Old MacDonald had a Woodshop* and "Sleep, Baby, Sleep" (Teacher's Edition, p. 197). Both texts are kinds of songs. *Old MacDonald had a Woodshop* is a sing-along song, and "Sleep, Baby, Sleep" is a lullaby. Imagine that there will be a school dance. Write a letter to the principal of your school persuading him/her to play one of the songs. Give your opinion and reasons for choosing that song. Remember to use persuasive words.

Think Aloud Your ideas will be more convincing if they are well organized. Decide on the opinion, or claim, you will state in your letter. Then decide what facts, details, and examples from the texts you will use to support your opinion. Let's fill in a chart before you begin writing to organize your thoughts.

Guided Writing Display a chart with three or four boxes as an example. Show children how to write their opinion in the first box in the sentence frame: _____ *is a better song than* _____. Then they can write one or two ideas that support their opinion in the other boxes using the sentence frame: *I think it is a better song because* _____. (If children have more than one reason, tell them to put their reasons in order with the most important reason first.) Next they can influence the reader's attitude and actions by using the sentence frame: *You should play it at the school dance because* _____.

STEP 3 Draft Your Writing

Have children use their charts to write a persuasive letter. Remind them of the key features of a persuasive letter. Tell them to write *Dear _____,* (with the principal's name on the line and a comma after it). On the next line down, they will begin their letter with their opinion. After writing their opinion and reasons, they may write *Sincerely,* and then their name.

Think Aloud One of the best ways to share opinions is to support them with facts and details. You can find facts and details by reviewing *Old MacDonald had a Woodshop* and "Sleep, Baby, Sleep." You can also look at the pictures in the selections to help you decide which is a better song.

Getting Started Tell children to write their persuasive letter using the chart to keep them on track. First they will give their opinion. Then they will use facts, reasons, and examples for support. They will try to influence the reader's attitude and actions. Emphasize the importance of using correct grammar and complete sentences.

STEP 4 Evaluate Your Writing

Display the checklist below and have children use it to evaluate their persuasive letters. Circulate around the room and confer with individual children.

- ✓ Did I state my opinion clearly?
- ✓ Do my reasons, facts, or examples support my opinion?
- ✓ Did I use persuasive words to influence people's attitudes and actions?
- ✓ Did I use correct letter format and conventions?

Help children set goals and make a plan for improving in areas where their writing needs help.

STEP 5 Revise and Publish

Help children follow through with their plans for revision. If time permits, have children sing along to the song they wrote about.

Publishing Children can publish their letter by presenting it to the principal.

More Connect the Texts
Opinion Letter

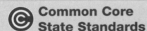 **Common Core State Standards**

Writing 1. Use a combination of drawing, dictating, and writing to compose opinion pieces in which they tell a reader the topic or the name of the book they are writing about and state an opinion or preference about the topic or book (e.g., *My favorite book is . . .*). **Writing 8.** With guidance and support from adults, recall information from experiences or gather information from provided sources to answer a question.

STEP 1 Read Like a Writer

Review the key features of an opinion letter listed below. Respond to any questions children might have.

Key Features of an Opinion Letter
- States the writer's opinion about a topic
- Supports the opinion with reasons, facts, and examples
- Uses descriptive words to make writing more convincing
- Often organizes reasons in order of importance
- Uses correct letter format and conventions

Choose an opinion letter that children have already read to model key features. Display the model for children to see and point out each of the key features you have discussed.

STEP 2 Organize Your Ideas

Writing Prompt Look back at *Alistair and Kip's Great Adventure* and *Old MacDonald had a Woodshop*. Both stories are about animals making things. Pick your favorite animal from the stories and write a letter to a classmate explaining why that animal is your favorite. Use reasons and examples from the text.

Think Aloud Your ideas will be more convincing if they are well organized. Decide on the opinion, or claim, you will state in your letter. Then decide what facts, details, and examples from the texts you will use to support your opinion. Let's brainstorm ideas on the board before you begin writing to organize your thoughts.

Guided Writing Write children's ideas on the board so they can copy them. Show children how to write their opinion using the sentence frame: *My favorite animal is the _____.* Then they can write one or two ideas that support their opinion using the sentence frame: *The _____ is my favorite animal because _____.* (If children have more than one reason, tell them to put their reasons in order with the most important reason first.)

STEP 3 Draft Your Writing

Have children use the sentence frames and ideas from the board to write an opinion letter. Remind them of the key features of an opinion letter. Tell them to write *Dear* _____, (with their classmate's name on the line and a comma after it). On the next line down, they will begin their letter with their opinion. After writing their opinion and reasons, they should write *Sincerely,* and then their name.

Think Aloud One of the best ways to share opinions is to use facts and details as support. You can find facts and details by reviewing *Alistair and Kip's Great Adventure* and *Old MacDonald had a Woodshop.* You can also look at books, articles, and Web sites to find additional facts about the animal you chose.

Getting Started Tell children to write their opinion letter using the sentence frames and ideas from the board to keep them on track. First they will give their opinion. Then they will use facts, reasons, and examples for support. They can practice writing their sentences before they write the final letter.

STEP 4 Evaluate Your Writing

Display the checklist below and have children use it to evaluate their opinion letters. Circulate around the room and confer with individual children.

✓ Did I state my opinion clearly?
✓ Do my reasons, facts, or examples support my opinion?
✓ Did I use descriptive words to make my writing more convincing?
✓ Did I use correct letter format and conventions?

Help children set goals and make a plan for improving in areas where their writing needs help.

STEP 5 Revise and Publish

Help children follow through with their plans for revision. If time permits, have children draw a picture to accompany their letter.

Publishing Children can publish their letter by presenting it to the classmate they wrote to.

More Connect the Texts
Opinion Paragraph

Objectives

- Identify the characteristics of an opinion paragraph.
- Write an opinion paragraph, using an opinion and one or two supporting details.
- Evaluate your writing.
- Revise and publish your writing.

 Common Core State Standards

Writing 1. Use a combination of drawing, dictating, and writing to compose opinion pieces in which they tell a reader the topic or the name of the book they are writing about and state an opinion or preference about the topic or book (e.g., *My favorite book is . . .*). **Writing 8.** With guidance and support from adults, recall information from experiences or gather information from provided sources to answer a question.

STEP 1 Read Like a Writer

Review the key features of an opinion paragraph listed below. Respond to any questions children might have.

Key Features of an Opinion Paragraph
- States the writer's opinion about a topic
- Supports the opinion with reasons, facts, or examples
- Uses descriptive words to make writing more convincing
- Often organizes reasons in order of importance
- Uses correct paragraph format and conventions

Choose an opinion piece that children have already read to model key features. Display the model for children to see and point out each of the key features you have discussed.

STEP 2 Organize Your Ideas

Writing Prompt Look back at *The House That Tony Lives In* and "Two Kinds of Homes" (Teacher's Edition, p. 99). Both stories are about houses and how they are built. Would you want to live in a house like Tony's, a pueblo, or a tipi? Write a sentence to tell which home you would want to live in. Then write a sentence to explain your reasons for choosing that home, using examples from the texts.

Think Aloud Your ideas will be more convincing if they are well organized. Decide on the opinion, or claim, you will state in your paragraph. Then decide what facts, reasons, and examples from the texts you will use to support your opinion. Let's brainstorm some words and sentences on the board before we get started.

Guided Writing Write these sentence frames on the board: *I would want to live in a _____.* Explain that this is their opinion. Now they will write a reason from the texts for their opinion. *I would want to live in this type of home because _____.* If children have more than one reason, tell them to put their reasons in order with the most important first. Continue to help children think of descriptive words and phrases to use in their paragraphs. Write them on the board for children to copy.

STEP 3 Draft Your Writing

Have children review the selections and pick the home they would most like to live in. They can copy some of the words from the selections and from the board. Have them practice using correct paragraph format and conventions.

Think Aloud The best way to support your opinion is to use facts, reasons, or examples. You can find facts and details by reviewing *The House That Tony Lives In* and "Two Kinds of Homes." Look at the illustrations. You may find details that will help with your reasons.

Getting Started Tell children to begin writing their opinion paragraph using the sentence frames from the board to keep them on track. First, they will write their opinion. Then they will use facts, reasons, and examples for support. They can practice writing their letters and sentences before they write the final paragraph.

STEP 4 Evaluate Your Writing

Display the checklist below and have children use it to evaluate their opinion paragraphs. Circulate around the room and confer with individual children.

- ✓ Did I state my opinion clearly?
- ✓ Do my reasons, facts, or examples support my opinion?
- ✓ Did I use descriptive words to make my writing more convincing?
- ✓ Did I use correct paragraph format and conventions?

Help children set goals and make a plan for improving in areas where their writing needs help.

STEP 5 Revise and Publish

Help children follow through with their plans for revision. If time permits, have children draw a picture of the home they chose.

Publishing Children can publish their opinion paragraph by presenting it and their drawing to the class.

More Connect the Texts
Animal Fantasy

Objectives

- Identify the characteristics of an animal fantasy.
- Write an animal fantasy with a beginning, middle, and end.
- Tell how you feel about what happens in the story.
- Evaluate your writing.
- Revise and publish your writing.

 Common Core State Standards

Writing 3. Use a combination of drawing, dictating, and writing to narrate a single event or several loosely linked events, tell about the events in the order in which they occurred, and provide a reaction to what happened. **Writing 8.** With guidance and support from adults, recall information from experiences or gather information from provided sources to answer a question.

STEP 1 Read Like a Writer

Review the key features of an animal fantasy listed below. Respond to any questions children might have.

Key Features of an Animal Fantasy

- Characters are animals
- Events are make-believe
- Characters do things that real animals cannot do
- Focuses on one event or several events
- Puts the events in order

Choose a fantasy story that children have already read to model key features. Display the model for children to see and point out each of the key features you have discussed.

STEP 2 Organize Your Ideas

Writing Prompt Look back at *Plaidypus Lost* and *Miss Bindergarten Takes a Field Trip with Kindergarten. Miss Bindergarten* is an animal fantasy where the animals take a trip through the city. Write a story in which Plaidypus goes with them and how he feels. What kind of adventures do you think he could have? Choose one of the places the kindergarten class visited to be the setting for the story.

Think Aloud First, let's share our ideas about what happens to Plaidypus on his trip with kindergarten. I will write your ideas, and we will choose one to develop with more details. We will write four sentences about the event, describing the setting and how Plaidypus feels. Then everyone will copy the sentences onto their paper.

Guided Writing As you write the sentences, talk about how a sentence is structured with a capital letter beginning the first word of a sentence and ending the sentence with a period. If multiple events happen, remind children that the events need to be written in order.

STEP 3 Draft Your Writing

Continue to discuss what children think will happen to Plaidypus. Have them watch as you put things in sequential order and add descriptive phrases.

Think Aloud One of the ways to make our story more interesting is to add descriptive details to our sentences. For example, if Plaidypus is *running,* he could be *running fast.* In *Miss Bindergarten,* Patricia steers a *canvas cart* instead of just a *cart.* As we discuss what will happen to Plaidypus, think of details to make the story more interesting.

Getting Started Have children copy the story onto their papers, being aware of the order of the words and carefully taking time to form each letter correctly. Have them complete the final sentence frame. Allow enough time for children to develop and draw an illustration for the story they have created.

STEP 4 Evaluate Your Writing

Display the checklist below and have children use it to evaluate the animal fantasy. Circulate around the room and confer with individual children.

> ✓ Did I introduce my character at the beginning?
> ✓ Did I focus on one event or several events?
> ✓ Did I put the events in order?
> ✓ Did I tell how I feel about what happens in the story?
> ✓ Did I describe the event with some details to make it interesting?

Help children set goals and make a plan for improving in areas where their writing needs help.

STEP 5 Revise and Publish

Help children follow through with their plans for revision. They should practice writing the sentences a few times to become more familiar with the shape of the letters and how the words are put together in a sentence. After the stories are published, ask children to share how they feel about their stories.

Publishing Children can publish their stories by hanging them around the room.

Personal Narrative

Objectives

- Identify the characteristics of a personal narrative.
- Write a story about yourself.
- Put the events in order.
- Evaluate your writing.
- Revise and publish your writing.

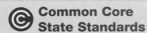

Common Core State Standards

Writing 3. Use a combination of drawing, dictating, and writing to narrate a single event or several loosely linked events, tell about the events in the order in which they occurred, and provide a reaction to what happened. **Writing 8.** With guidance and support from adults, recall information from experiences or gather information from provided sources to answer a question.

STEP 1 Read Like a Writer

Review the key features of a personal narrative listed below. Respond to any questions children might have.

Key Features of a Personal Narrative

- Focuses on one incident or event
- Tells a story about yourself as the main character
- Tells a story in the order in which it occurs
- Tells how the writer feels about what happens in the story

Choose a personal narrative that children have already read to model key features. Display the model for children to see and point out each of the key features you have discussed.

STEP 2 Organize Your Ideas

Writing Prompt Look back at *Smash! Crash!* and *Dig Dig Digging.* Imagine that you are on the street in one of these stories. Write a new story about what you saw and how you felt about it. Look through the stories to find details to make your narrative more interesting. Write these words in a list to use later as you write.

Think Aloud Let's think about what all the trucks do, how they look, and what noises they make. I will write your ideas so you can copy the words and phrases into your sentences. This is a story about you, so think about something that you saw as a character in the story.

Guided Writing You could start with the sentence frames: *I saw _____. It was _____. Then it _____.* or *I rode in a _____. It went _____. Then it _____.* Remind children that the events need to be written in order, and it will help make their writing more interesting to use some details.

STEP 3 Draft Your Writing

Continue to discuss with children their ideas for their stories. Point out descriptive words in *Smash! Crash!* such as *louder, larger, huge,* and *strong.* Point out action words in *Dig Dig Digging,* such as *flashing, racing, lifting,* and *spinning.*

Think Aloud One of the ways to make your story more interesting is to add descriptive details to your sentences. In *Dig Dig Digging,* pipes are *slowly spinning.* Fire engines have *bright lights flashing.* These words help us picture the events happening in real life. Now let's think of some special words for your stories.

Getting Started Have children copy the sentence frames onto their papers. Remind them to be aware of the order of the words and how to form each letter correctly. Have them copy some words from the board or use the books to complete their sentences. If there is enough time, children can create an illustration for their story.

STEP 4 Evaluate Your Writing

Display the checklist below and have children use it to evaluate their personal narratives. Circulate around the room and confer with individual children.

- ✓ Did I tell a story about myself as the main character?
- ✓ Did I focus on one event?
- ✓ Did I tell a story in the order in which it occurs?
- ✓ Did I describe the event with some details to make it interesting?
- ✓ Did I tell how I feel about what happens in the story?

Help children set goals and make a plan for improving in areas where their writing needs help.

STEP 5 Revise and Publish

Help children follow through with their plans for revision. Have them practice writing the sentences a few times to become more familiar with the shape of the letters and how the words are put together in a sentence. If time permits, have children share their stories.

Publishing Children can publish their stories by hanging them around the room or you can make a classroom book.

More Connect the Texts
Animal Fantasy

Objectives

- Identify the characteristics of an animal fantasy.
- Write an animal fantasy with a beginning, middle, and end.
- Focus on one event or several events.
- Put the events in order.
- Evaluate your writing.
- Revise and publish your writing.

Common Core State Standards

Writing 3. Use a combination of drawing, dictating, and writing to narrate a single event or several loosely linked events, tell about the events in the order in which they occurred, and provide a reaction to what happened. **Writing 8.** With guidance and support from adults, recall information from experiences or gather information from provided sources to answer a question.

STEP 1   Read Like a Writer

Review the key features of an animal fantasy listed below. Respond to any questions children might have.

Key Features of an Animal Fantasy
- Has characters that are animals
- Presents events that are make-believe
- Has events that happen in order
- Has characters that do things real animals cannot do
- Has characters, plot, and a setting

Choose an animal fantasy that children have already read to model key features. Display the model for children to see and point out each of the key features you have discussed.

STEP 2   Organize Your Ideas

Writing Prompt Look back at "At the Bus Stop" (Teacher's Edition, p. 27) and *The Little School Bus*. "At the Bus Stop" is a realistic narrative about a brother and a sister who wait for a school bus, and *The Little School Bus* is an animal fantasy about animals that take the bus to school. Write a story in which Ana and Jay get picked up by the school bus and find the funny animals sitting in the seats.

Think Aloud First, let's remind ourselves who the characters are in *The Little School Bus.* Do you think a boy and a girl would find it funny to watch these characters on the bus? Let's talk about your favorite characters. What do they look like and what are they wearing? I will write these descriptions on the board. What do you think Ana and Jay would say to your favorite character? What would they say to each other?

Guided Writing Review children's descriptions on the board. Have children start their story with *Ana and Jay* _____. Tell them to use *The Little School Bus* to find names and words to describe the characters. Have them tell what happens when Ana and Jay talk to a character.

STEP 3 Draft Your Writing

Continue to discuss what children think will happen to Ana and Jay as they get on the bus. Have them make a list of the events in the order that they happen.

Think Aloud One of the ways to make our story more interesting is to add describing words, or details, to our sentences: The goat wears a *new winter* coat. The *hairy* bear has *messy* hair. When you imagine what is happening to Ana and Jay, think of details to describe where they are, what they see, and what they do.

Getting Started Have children write two or three sentences on their papers. Review how a sentence begins with a capital letter and ends with a period. Remind them to carefully write their letters and to keep a space between each word. If time permits, invite children to draw a picture of Ana and Jay with one of the animal characters.

STEP 4 Evaluate Your Writing

Display the checklist below and have children use it to evaluate the animal fantasy. Circulate around the room and confer with individual children.

✓ Did I introduce my characters at the beginning?

✓ Did I focus on one event or several events?

✓ Did I put the events in order?

✓ Did I describe the event with some details to make it interesting?

Help children set goals and make a plan for improving in areas where their writing needs help.

STEP 5 Revise and Publish

Help children follow through with their plans for revision. Have them practice writing the sentences a few times to become more familiar with the shape of the letters and how the words are put together in a sentence.

Publishing Children can publish their stories by posting them around the room, or you could collect them into a class storybook.

More Connect the Texts
Animal Fantasy

Objectives

- Identify the characteristics of an animal fantasy.
- Write an animal fantasy with a beginning, middle, and end.
- Tell how you feel about what happens in the story.
- Evaluate your writing.
- Revise and publish your writing.

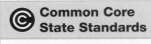

Common Core State Standards

Writing 3. Use a combination of drawing, dictating, and writing to narrate a single event or several loosely linked events, tell about the events in the order in which they occurred, and provide a reaction to what happened. **Writing 8.** With guidance and support from adults, recall information from experiences or gather information from provided sources to answer a question.

STEP 1 Read Like a Writer

Review the key features of an animal fantasy listed below. Respond to any questions children might have.

Key Features of an Animal Fantasy

- Characters are animals
- Events are make-believe
- Characters do things that real animals cannot do
- Focuses on one event or several events
- Puts the events in order

Choose a fantasy story that children have already read to model key features. Display the model for children to see and point out each of the key features you have discussed.

STEP 2 Organize Your Ideas

Writing Prompt Look back at *Bear Snores On* and *A Bed for the Winter.* *Bear Snores On* is an animal fantasy in which the animals escape a storm in Bear's cave and have a party. *A Bed for the Winter* explains how a dormouse finds a good winter home. You have written an invitation to the dormouse to come to a party. Now write a story about the dormouse at the party.

Think Aloud First, let's share our ideas about what happens when the dormouse comes to the cave for a party. What does she bring? Share what happens at parties you go to. I will write some of your ideas on the board. We will also put what happens first in the beginning of the story. Then we will write what happens next. This is called *sequence*. Sequence makes it easier to understand what happens in a story.

Guided Writing As you write the sentences, talk about what the title of this story will be. Remind children that when they are telling a story, the events need to happen in order. Discuss what happens in the beginning, the middle, and at the end.

STEP 3 Draft Your Writing

Continue to discuss what children think will happen at the party. Remind children to think of details that would make their stories more interesting and to put the events in order.

Think Aloud One of the ways to make our story more interesting is to add descriptive details to our sentences. For example, the dormouse brings a cake to the party. It could be a *big* cake or a *sweet* cake. You can add words to make the story more interesting.

Getting Started Have children copy the story onto their papers, being aware of the order of the words and taking their time to form each letter correctly. Have them write three or four sentences. Allow enough time for children to develop and execute an illustration for the story they have created.

STEP 4 Evaluate Your Writing

Display the checklist below and have children use it to evaluate the animal fantasy. Circulate around the room and confer with individual children.

✓ Did I introduce my character at the beginning?

✓ Did I focus on one event or several events?

✓ Did I put the events in order?

✓ Did I describe the event with some details to make it interesting?

✓ Did I include a title at the beginning of the story?

Help children set goals and make a plan for improving in areas where their writing needs help.

STEP 5 Revise and Publish

Help children follow through with their plans for revision. They should practice writing the sentences a few times to become more familiar with the shape of the letters and how the words are put together in a sentence. After the stories are published, ask children how they feel about their stories.

Publishing Children can publish their stories by reading them to one of their classmates.

More Connect the Texts
Personal Narrative

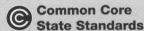

Common Core State Standards

Writing 3. Use a combination of drawing, dictating, and writing to narrate a single event or several loosely linked events, tell about the events in the order in which they occurred, and provide a reaction to what happened. **Writing 8.** With guidance and support from adults, recall information from experiences or gather information from provided sources to answer a question.

STEP 1 Read Like a Writer

Review the key features of a personal narrative listed below. Respond to any questions children might have.

Key Features of a Personal Narrative

- Is about an interesting experience in the writer's life
- Tells the story using *I* or *me*
- Flows from beginning to middle to end
- Provides details to make the event vivid
- Provides a reaction to what happens in the story

Choose a personal narrative that children have already read to model key features. Display the model for children to see and point out each of the key features you have discussed.

STEP 2 Organize Your Ideas

Writing Prompt Look back at *Flowers* and *Nature Spy*. Both of these selections describe things that happen or what you are able to see in nature. Write a story about yourself and what you see on a walk around your neighborhood.

Think Aloud Let's share our ideas about what we see as we take a walk. We can look back at *Flowers* and *Nature Spy* to find ideas. The photographs in both selections will also provide us with descriptive images to make our writing more exciting.

Guided Writing First, write a list of things that children see on their walks. You can talk about what kind of day it is, where they may be going, and what they may see on their walks. As you write sentences, ask children if there are ways the items listed could be better described. If they see trees, are they *tall* trees, *green* trees, or *pine* trees?

STEP 3 Draft Your Writing

Continue to discuss what children see on their walks. Remind children to think of descriptive images to make their writing more interesting. Also emphasize they should put things in sequential order.

Think Aloud As we write our stories, we need to write the events in the order they happen. Use the linking words *first, next, second, then,* or *finally.*

Getting Started Have children copy the story onto their papers, being aware of the order of the events and using descriptive details. With their final sentence, ask them to write how they feel about their walk. Did they have a good time? If there is time, children can draw an illustration for the story they have written.

STEP 4 Evaluate Your Writing

Display the checklist below and have children use it to evaluate their personal narrative. Circulate around the room and confer with individual children.

✓ Is this about an interesting experience in my life?
✓ Does the story use *I* or *me?*
✓ Does the story flow from beginning to middle to end?
✓ Does the story provide details to make the event vivid?
✓ Did I include a reaction to what happens in the story?

Help children set goals and make a plan for improving in areas where their writing needs help.

STEP 5 Revise and Publish

Help children follow through with their plans for revision. They should practice writing the sentences a few times to become more familiar with the shape of the letters and how the words are put together in a sentence.

Publishing Children can publish their stories by hanging them around the room, sharing them with the class, or making a class book.

More Connect the Texts
Personal Narrative

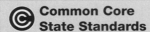
STEP 1 Read Like a Writer

Review the key features of a personal narrative listed below. Respond to any questions children might have.

Key Features of a Personal Narrative

- Tells a story about yourself, including the plot and the setting
- Focuses on one or more incidents or events
- Tells events in the order they occurred
- Uses correct sentence format and conventions

Choose a personal narrative that children have already read to model key features. Display the model for children to see and point at each of the key features you have discussed.

STEP 2 Organize Your Ideas

Writing Prompt Look back at *Little Quack* and *Farfallina and Marcel.* These stories are about characters who are growing up. Like the characters in these stories, you are growing up too. Write a story about something you learned to do that you couldn't do when you were younger.

Think Aloud Organize your ideas to make them more clear. Think about something you learned to do. Think about how you did it. Let's brainstorm some sentences and phrases you can use in your stories.

Guided Writing Write sentence frames on the board for children to copy. First, they can tell readers who the story is about and when and what they learned to do. *A few _____s ago, I learned to _____.* Then children can describe how they learned to do it. *When I was younger, I could not _____. I practiced _____. Now I can _____.* Continue to help children brainstorm words and phrases they can use in their stories.

STEP 3 Draft Your Writing

Have children use their sentence frames to write a personal narrative. Remind them of the key features of a personal narrative.

Think Aloud The best way to describe the events in your story is to put them in order. You can review *Little Quack* and *Farfallina and Marcel* to help you put events in order. You can also look at other stories to get ideas about how to describe the things that you did.

Getting Started Tell children to begin writing using the sentence frames to keep them on track. Remind them to focus on something they have learned to do that they could not do when they were younger. Emphasize the importance of using complete sentences.

STEP 4 Evaluate Your Writing

Display the checklist below and have children use it to evaluate their personal narrative. Circulate around the room and confer with individual children.

✓ Did I tell a story about myself and include the plot and the setting?

✓ Did I clearly describe the events?

✓ Did I put the events in order?

✓ Did I use correct sentence format and conventions?

Help children set goals and make a plan for improving in areas where their writing needs help.

STEP 5 Revise and Publish

Help children follow through with their plans for revision and carefully write their sentences on a clean sheet of paper.

Publishing Children can publish their stories by reading them to each other.

More Connect the Texts
Animal Fantasy

Objectives

- Identify the characteristics of an animal fantasy.
- Write about a make-believe event.
- Evaluate your writing.
- Revise and publish your writing with a picture.

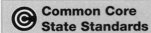

Common Core State Standards

Writing 3. Use a combination of drawing, dictating, and writing to narrate a single event or several loosely linked events, tell about the events in the order in which they occurred, and provide a reaction to what happened.

STEP 1 Read Like a Writer

Review the key features of an animal fantasy listed below. Respond to any questions children might have.

Key Features of an Animal Fantasy

- Characters are animals
- Events are make-believe
- Characters do things that real animals cannot do
- Uses correct sentence conventions

Choose an animal fantasy that children have already read to model key features. Display the model for children to see and point out each of the key features you have discussed.

STEP 2 Organize Your Ideas

Writing Prompt Look back at *Farfallina and Marcel* and "How Coyote Helped People" (Teacher's Edition, p. 495). Both of these stories are animal fantasies, or make-believe stories. Both have animal characters. Imagine that Coyote ran down the mountain and stopped at the pond where Farfallina and Marcel lived. What would the new friends do together? Write two or three sentences that tell about the characters and an event. Illustrate your animal fantasy with a picture of the three friends having fun.

Think Aloud Let's talk about the setting of these stories. What are some activities that the friends could do together at the pond? Remember that in animal fantasies, the characters do things that real animals cannot do. Think about what you like to do with your friends. I will record your ideas on the board so you can use those verbs and phrases in your stories.

Guided Writing Write these sentence frames on the board to introduce the characters: ____ *and* ___ *lived at the pond. Then they met* _____. Children can use the characters' names—Farfallina, Marcel, and Coyote—or they can simply use *the butterfly, the goose,* and *the coyote.* They can use verbs in this sentence frame: *They have fun* ____ *together.*

STEP 3 Draft Your Writing

Have children review the names of the characters they will be writing about and think of activities the three friends could do together at the pond. Children can copy verbs from the board to use in the sentence frames.

Think Aloud Remember that characters in an animal fantasy do things that real animals cannot do. These animals like to have fun, and they can play in the water or on the land.

Getting Started Tell children to write their sentences at the top of the page, leaving room at the bottom for their picture of the three characters.

STEP 4 Evaluate Your Writing

Display the checklist below and have children use it to evaluate their animal fantasy. Circulate around the room and confer with individual children.

✓ Did I name the characters?

✓ Did I describe an event?

✓ Did I use correct letter formation and sentence conventions?

Help children set goals and make a plan for improving in areas where their writing needs help.

STEP 5 Revise and Publish

Help children follow through with their plans for revision and carefully write their sentences under the picture.

Publishing Children can publish their stories by reading them to each other.

More Connect the Texts
Fable

Objectives

- Identify the characteristics of a fable.
- Write a fable about animal characters.
- Evaluate your writing.
- Revise and publish your writing.

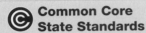

Common Core State Standards

Writing 3. Use a combination of drawing, dictating, and writing to narrate a single event or several loosely linked events, tell about the events in the order in which they occurred, and provide a reaction to what happened.

STEP 1 Read Like a Writer

Review the key features of a fable listed below. Respond to any questions children might have.

Key Features of a Fable

- Has characters, a plot, and a setting
- Teaches a moral, or a lesson
- Uses logical order of events
- Uses correct story format and conventions

Choose a fable that children have already read to model key features. Display the model for children to see and point out each of the key features you have discussed.

STEP 2 Organize Your Ideas

Writing Prompt Look back at "The Mice and the Cat" (Teacher's Edition, p. 397) and *The Lion and the Mouse.* Both of these stories are fables about mice who try to solve a problem. Imagine that the lion comes to live with the mice and protect them from the cat. Write a new fable about the cat. Who will the cat chase? Who will be his friend? What lesson does he learn?

Think Aloud Your ideas will be more interesting if they are well organized. Think about the way the cat feels now that the lion is in the house protecting the mice. Think about how he can make himself feel better. Let's fill in a chart before you begin writing to organize your thoughts.

Guided Writing Display a chart with four boxes as an example. Show children how to introduce the characters and the setting in the first box with the sentence frames: *The cat spent his time chasing and scaring the mice. He loved to do this because _____. One of his favorite things to do was _____.* Next, the children can tell about the lion. *Then the lion came to live with the mice and protect them from the cat. The lion told the cat _____. The cat was afraid of the lion. He became bored and lonely because _____.* Last, children can tell how the story ends and the lesson the cat learns. *One day, the sad cat told the mice that _____. The mice and the lion talked it over and decided _____. This made the cat feel _____. He learned that it feels better to _____.*

STEP 3 Draft Your Writing

Have children review characters they will be writing about and think about the events. Brainstorm ideas about what the characters say to each other and how they feel. Remember that fables involve a lesson, or moral. Children can copy words and phrases written on the board to use in the sentence frames.

Think Aloud The best way to describe the events in your fable is to put them in order. You can review "The Mice and the Cat" and *The Lion and the Mouse* to help you put events in order. You can also look at other stories to get ideas about characters and lessons in fables.

Getting Started Tell children to write their sentences at the top of the page, leaving room at the bottom for a picture of a character or event from their fable.

STEP 4 Evaluate Your Writing

Display the checklist below and have children use it to evaluate their fable. Circulate around the room and confer with individual children.

> ✓ Did I name the animal characters, plot, and setting?
> ✓ Does my fable teach a lesson, or moral?
> ✓ Did I put the events in order?
> ✓ Did I use the correct story format and conventions?

Help children set goals and make a plan for improving in areas where their writing needs help.

STEP 5 Revise and Publish

Help children follow through with their plans for revision and carefully write their sentences above the picture.

Publishing Children can publish their fables by reading them to the class or compiling them in a class book.

More Connect the Texts
Animal Fantasy

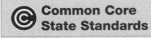
STEP 1 Read Like a Writer

Review the key features of an animal fantasy listed below. Respond to any questions children might have.

Key Features of an Animal Fantasy
- Has characters that are animals, a plot, and a setting
- Focuses on one or more incidents or events
- Tells events in the order they occur
- Characters do things that real animals cannot do

Choose an animal fantasy that children have already read to model key features. Display the model for children to see and point out each of the key features you have discussed.

STEP 2 Organize Your Ideas

Writing Prompt Look back at *My Lucky Day* and *Goldilocks and the Three Bears.* They are both animal fantasies because some of the main characters are animals that can speak and act like humans do. Think about what would happen if the piglet went to the three bears' house. Which porridge would he eat? Which chair would he sit in? Which bed would he sleep in? Tell readers to identify the main character and the setting. Focus on a couple of events and put them in order.

Think Aloud Your ideas will be more interesting if they are well organized. Think about what the piglet will do when he goes to the three bears' house. Think about which porridge, chair, and bed he will like best. Let's brainstorm some sentences and phrases you can use in your animal fantasies.

Guided Writing Write sentence frames on the board for children to copy. First, children can tell readers about the main character and the setting. *When _____ was walking through the forest, he decided to go to _____.* Next, they can tell readers what the main character did. *First, the piglet tried the porridge. He liked _____'s porridge the best. Next, he sat in the chairs. The piglet liked _____'s chair the best. Then the piglet laid down in all of the beds. He liked _____'s bed the best.* Make sure children tell the events in order.

STEP 3 Draft Your Writing

Have children use their sentence frames to write an animal fantasy. Remind them of the key features of an animal fantasy.

Think Aloud The best way to describe the events in your animal fantasy is to put them in order. You can review *My Lucky Day* and *Goldilocks and the Three Bears* to help you put events in order. You can also look at other stories to get ideas about how to describe the events.

Getting Started Tell children to write their animal fantasy on a clean sheet of paper. If there is extra time, children can draw a picture of the piglet in the three bears' house.

STEP 4 Evaluate Your Writing

Display the checklist below and have children use it to evaluate their animal fantasy. Circulate around the room and confer with individual children.

- ✓ Did I tell an animal fantasy that has characters, a plot, and a setting?
- ✓ Did I clearly describe the events?
- ✓ Did I put the events in order?
- ✓ Did I use the correct sentence format and conventions?

Help children set goals and make a plan for improving in areas where their writing needs help.

STEP 5 Revise and Publish

Help children follow through with their plans for revision and carefully write their animal fantasies on a clean sheet of paper.

Publishing Children can publish their animal fantasies by sharing them with their classmates.

More Connect the Texts
Personal Narrative

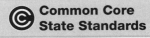 **Common Core State Standards**

Writing 3. Use a combination of drawing, dictating, and writing to narrate a single event or several loosely linked events, tell about the events in the order in which they occurred, and provide a reaction to what happened.

STEP 1 Read Like a Writer

Review the key features of a personal narrative listed below. Respond to any questions children might have.

Key Features of a Personal Narrative
- Is about an experience in the storyteller's life
- Focuses on one or more incidents or events
- Tells events in the order they occurred
- Uses correct sentence format and conventions

Choose a personal narrative that children have already read to model key features. Display the model for children to see and point out each of the key features you have discussed.

STEP 2 Organize Your Ideas

Writing Prompt Look back at *Rooster's Off to See the World* and *One Little Mouse.* In both of these stories, the main characters go on an adventure. Write a personal narrative about a time you went on an adventure. Whom did you go with? Where did you go? What did you do and see there? Identify the events and setting. Focus on one or two events and put them in order.

Think Aloud Your ideas will be more interesting if they are well organized. Think about your adventure. Identify the events and the setting. Tell the events in order. Let's brainstorm some sentences and phrases you can use in your stories.

Guided Writing Write sentence frames on the board for children to copy. First, they can tell readers who went on the adventure. _____ *and I decided to go on an adventure.* Next, the children can describe where they went. *We went on an adventure to _____.* Then children can tell the readers what they did and saw on their adventure. *On our adventure, we saw _____.* Continue to help children brainstorm ideas.

STEP 3 Draft Your Writing

Have children use their sentence frames to write a personal narrative. Remind them of the key features of a personal narrative.

Think Aloud The best way to describe the events in your personal narrative is to put them in order. You can review *Rooster's Off to See the World* and *One Little Mouse* to help you put events in order. You can also look at other stories to get ideas about how to describe the things that you saw and did.

Getting Started Tell children to write their personal narrative on a clean sheet of paper. If there is extra time, children can draw a picture of where they went and what they saw there.

STEP 4 Evaluate Your Writing

Display the checklist below and have children use it to evaluate their personal narrative. Circulate around the room and confer with individual children.

- ✓ Did I tell about an experience in my life?
- ✓ Did I clearly describe the events?
- ✓ Did I put the events in order?
- ✓ Did I use the sentence format and conventions?

Help children set goals and make a plan for improving in areas where their writing needs help.

STEP 5 Revise and Publish

Help children follow through with their plans for revision and carefully write their personal narratives on a clean sheet of paper.

Publishing Children can publish their personal narratives by reading them to each other.

More Connect the Texts
Story

Objectives

- Identify the characteristics of a story.
- Write a story that tells about one or more events in order.
- Evaluate your writing.
- Revise and publish your writing.

 Common Core State Standards

Writing 3. Use a combination of drawing, dictating, and writing to narrate a single event or several loosely linked events, tell about the events in the order in which they occurred, and provide a reaction to what happened. **Writing 8.** With guidance and support from adults, recall information from experiences or gather information from provided sources to answer a question.

STEP 1 Read Like a Writer

Review the key features of a story listed below. Respond to any questions children might have.

Key Features of a Story
- Has characters, setting, and plot
- Focuses on one or more events
- Tells about events in the order they occurred
- Uses correct sentence format and conventions

Choose a story that children have already heard of or read to model key features. Display the model for children to see and point out each of the key features you have discussed.

STEP 2 Organize Your Ideas

Writing Prompt Look back at *Max Takes the Train* and *The Little Engine That Could.* Both stories feature trains. Think about both trains. Write a story about what the trains would do together if they were friends. Where would they go? What would they see? Describe the characters, setting, and plot. Focus on telling about two or three events and put them in order.

Think Aloud Your ideas will be more interesting if they are well organized. Think about how the trains become friends and what they like to do together. Think about where they like to go. Let's brainstorm some sentences and phrases you can use in your stories.

Guided Writing Write sentence frames on the board for children to copy. First, they can introduce the characters and the setting. *The trains met one day on the tracks near _____.* Next, children can describe what the trains do together and the places they see. *The trains like to _____ together. Both trains travel to _____ and see _____.* Continue to help children brainstorm words and phrases they can use in their stories.

STEP 3 Draft Your Writing

Have children use the sentence frames to write a story. Remind them of the key features of a story.

Think Aloud The best way to describe the events in your story is to put them in the order in which they happen. You can review *Max Takes the Train* and *The Little Engine That Could* to help you put your events in order. You can also look at other stories to get ideas about what the two trains do together and the places they go.

Getting Started Tell children to write their sentences at the top of the page, leaving room at the bottom for their picture of the two trains.

STEP 4 Evaluate Your Writing

Display the checklist below and have children use it to evaluate their story. Circulate around the room and confer with individuals.

- ✓ Did I tell about my characters, setting, and plot?
- ✓ Did I clearly describe the events?
- ✓ Did I put the events in the order in which they happened?
- ✓ Did I use correct sentence format and conventions?

Help children set goals and make a plan for improving in areas where their writing needs help.

STEP 5 Revise and Publish

Help children follow through with their plans for revision and carefully write their sentences above their picture.

Publishing Children can publish their stories by reading them to one another.

More Connect the Texts
Fairy Tale

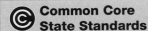
STEP 1 Read Like a Writer

Review the key features of a fairy tale listed below. Respond to any questions children might have.

Key Features of a Fairy Tale
- Has characters, setting, and plot
- Has characters that are either good or bad
- Focuses on one or more magical events
- Tells events in the order in which they occurred
- Uses correct sentence format and conventions

Choose a fairy tale that children have already heard or read to model key features. Display the model for children to see and point out each of the key features you have discussed.

STEP 2 Organize Your Ideas

Writing Prompt Look back at *Max Takes the Train* and "The Dragon Test" (Teacher's Edition, p. 609). Both of these stories are make-believe. *Max Takes the Train* is a fantasy, and "The Dragon Test" is a fairy tale. Imagine that Max and Ruby are the son and daughter of the king. How would Max try to slay the dragon? How would Ruby try to slay the dragon? Who would succeed? Tell what happens. Put your events in the order in which they happen.

Think Aloud Your ideas will be more interesting if they are well organized. Think about the way Max would try to slay the dragon. Think about the way Ruby would try to slay the dragon. Use examples from the text. Let's fill in a chart before you begin writing to organize your thoughts.

Guided Writing Display a chart with four boxes. Show children how to introduce the characters and setting in the first box using the sentence frame: *The king told his son _____ and his daughter _____ that whoever could slay the dragon would become the new ruler of the land.* Next, children can describe how Max and Ruby try to slay the dragon. *Max tried to slay the dragon by _____. Ruby tried to slay the dragon by _____.* Suggest to children that they make one character a bad character who fails and the other character a good character who succeeds. Last, children can tell who is successful. *_____ could not slay the dragon. So _____ will become the new ruler of the land!*

STEP 3 Draft Your Writing

Have children review characters they will be writing about and think of the way that each character would try to slay the dragon. Remind children that fairy tales have magical events. Brainstorm ideas and write them on the board. Children can copy words and phrases from the board to use in the sentence frames.

Think Aloud The best way to describe the events in your fairy tale is to put them in the order in which they happen. You can review *Max Takes the Train* and "The Dragon Test" to help you put your events in order. You can also look at other stories to get ideas about characters in fairy tales.

Getting Started Tell children to write their sentences at the top of the page, leaving room at the bottom for their picture of the character who succeeds wearing a crown.

STEP 4 Evaluate Your Writing

Display the checklist below and have children use it to evaluate their fairy tales. Circulate around the room and confer with individuals.

- ✓ Did I tell about my characters, setting, and plot?
- ✓ Did I include a good character and a bad character?
- ✓ Did I describe one or more magical events?
- ✓ Did I put the events in the order in which they happen?
- ✓ Did I use the correct sentence format and conventions?

Help children set goals and make a plan for improving in areas where their writing needs help.

STEP 5 Revise and Publish

Help children follow through with their plans for revision and carefully write their sentences above the picture.

Publishing Children can publish their fairy tales by reading them aloud to the class.

More Connect the Texts
Personal Narrative

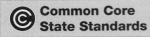
STEP 1 Read Like a Writer

Review the key features of a personal narrative listed below. Respond to any questions children might have.

Key Features of a Personal Narrative

- Tells about an incident in the writer's life
- Focuses on one or more events
- Tells events in the order they occurred
- Uses correct sentence format and conventions

Choose a personal narrative that children have already seen to model key features. Display the model for children and point out each of the key features you have discussed.

STEP 2 Organize Your Ideas

Writing Prompt Look back at *Building with Dad* and *The House That Tony Lives In.* In both of these stories, people are building and making things. Write a personal narrative about a time when you built or made something. What was it? Who helped you? Focus on one or two events and put them in order.

Think Aloud Your ideas will be more interesting if they are well organized. Think about something you built or made. Think about how you did it and who you worked with. Let's brainstorm some sentences and phrases you can use in your stories.

Guided Writing Write sentence frames on the board for children to copy. First, they can tell readers when and what was built or made. *A couple of _____s ago, I built/made _____ with_____.* Then the children can describe how they built or made it. *First, I _____. Then I _____. Last, I _____.* Continue to help children brainstorm words and phrases they can use in their stories.

STEP 3 Draft Your Writing

Have children use their sentence frames to write a personal narrative. Remind them of the key features of a personal narrative.

Think Aloud The best way to describe the events in your personal narrative is to put them in order. You can review *Building with Dad* and *The House That Tony Lives In* to help you put events in order. You can also look at other stories to get ideas about how to describe the things that you did.

Getting Started Tell children to write their personal narrative on a clean piece of paper. If there is extra time, children can draw a picture of what they made or built.

STEP 4 Evaluate Your Writing

Display the checklist below and have children use it to evaluate their personal narrative. Circulate around the room and confer with individual children.

- ✓ Did I tell a personal narrative that included an incident?
- ✓ Did I clearly describe the events?
- ✓ Did I put the events in order?
- ✓ Did I use the sentence format and conventions?

Help children set goals and make a plan for improving in areas where their writing needs help.

STEP 5 Revise and Publish

Help children follow through with their plans for revision and carefully write their sentences.

Publishing Children can publish their personal narratives by reading them to each other.

More Connect the Texts
Story

Objectives

- Identify the characteristics of a story.
- Write a story, including one or more events in order.
- Evaluate your writing.
- Revise and publish your writing.

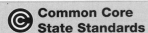

Common Core State Standards

Writing 3. Use a combination of drawing, dictating, and writing to narrate a single event or several loosely linked events, tell about the events in the order in which they occurred, and provide a reaction to what happened. **Writing 8.** With guidance and support from adults, recall information from experiences or gather information from provided sources to answer a question.

STEP 1 Read Like a Writer

Review the key features of a story listed below. Respond to any questions children might have.

Key Features of a Story

- Has characters, plot, and a setting
- Focuses on one or more incidents or events
- Tells events in the order they occurred
- Uses correct story format and conventions

Choose a story that children have already read to model key features. Display the model for children to see and point out each of the key features you discussed.

STEP 2 Organize Your Ideas

Writing Prompt Look back at "The Milkmaid and Her Pail" (Teacher's Edition, p. 297) and "Juan Bobo" (Teacher's Edition, p. 495). Both of these stories teach a lesson with characters from long ago. Think about if the milkmaid and Juan Bobo were friends. Write about what they would do together. Describe the characters, plot, and setting. Focus on one or two events and put them in order.

Think Aloud Your ideas will be more interesting if they are well organized. Think about how the milkmaid and Juan Bobo became friends and what they like to do together. Think about where they like to go. Let's brainstorm some sentences and phrases you can use in your stories.

Guided Writing Write sentence frames on the board for children to copy. First, they can introduce the characters and the setting. *The milkmaid and Juan Bobo met on the road near _____.* Next, the children can describe what they do together and the places they go. *The milkmaid and Juan Bobo have fun _____ together. They go to _____ and see _____.* Continue to help children brainstorm words and phrases they can use in their stories.

STEP 3 Draft Your Writing

Have children use the sentence frames to write a story. Remind them of the key features of a story.

Think Aloud The best way to describe the events in your story is to put them in order. You can review "The Milkmaid and Her Pail" and "Juan Bobo" to help you put events in order. You can also look at other stories to get ideas about what the characters do together and the places they go.

Getting Started Tell children to write their sentences at the top of the page, leaving room at the bottom for their picture of the two characters.

STEP 4 Evaluate Your Writing

Display the checklist below and have children use it to evaluate their story. Circulate around the room and confer with individual children.

   ✓ Did I name the characters, plot, and setting?
   ✓ Did I clearly describe the events?
   ✓ Did I put the events in order?
   ✓ Did I use the correct story format and conventions?

Help children set goals and make a plan for improving in areas where their writing needs help.

STEP 5 Revise and Publish

Help children follow through with their plans for revision and carefully write their sentences above the picture.

Publishing Children can publish their stories by reading them to each other.